Woomera

Its human face

Edward W. Chambers

Inquiries should be made to:

Seaview Press
PO Box 234
Henley Beach, South Australia 5022
Telephone 08 8235 1535; fax 08 8235 9144
E-mail: seaview@seaviewpress.com.au
Web site: http://www.seaviewpress.com.au

Printed by:
Copy Master
234 Currie Street
Adelaide, South Australia 5000

National Library of Australia Cataloguing-in-Publication data

Chambers, Edward W.
Woomera : its human face.

ISBN 1 74008 061 0

1. Rockets (Aeronautics) - Research - South Australia -
Woomera. 2. Weapons - Research - South Australia - Woomera.
3. Aeronautical engineers - South Australia - Woomera -
Anecdotes. 4. Woomera (S. Aust.) - History - Anecdotes.
5. Woomera (S. Aust.) - History - Humor. I. Title.

994.238

Contents

To the Skylark launch team
1969 - 1978

Foreword

I, the writer of the following chronicle of things rocket, had the privilege of some twenty five years in their company, including the people who made them and also those bold enough to fly them.

It was an experience full of technical interest, friendships which have spanned 12,000 miles, moments of high drama and times of good humour.

I hope that the words that follow give evidence of each of the above aspects of the human condition. The story starts with my departure from Sydney in late 1952, followed by the rocket affair which began in Bristol, England, with the historic Bristol Aeroplane Company.

From 1956 onwards the scene moves to South Australia and predominantly to Woomera where I had an active involvement with the rocket world until about the end of 1978, when it can be said with some confidence that Woomera's last significant British rocket firing took place.

There is little doubt that life with rockets was a very special existence. Likewise, little doubt that the Woomera Village and its unique Rocket Range were also very special places.

Edward W. Chambers 2000

Chronological note

The events described under the following headings all took place between 1953 and 1978. They recall strong memories of the rockets and men and women I was privileged to know.

I have written only of those things and projects in which I had direct involvement. While these were unfolding, there were many other rocket projects taking advantage of what the Woomera Range had to offer — in truth a veritable kaleidoscope of things that took off with a bang and landed with a bump on the ancient and generally unyielding, desert "donga".

A short list of such rockets/missiles would include UK ones like —

*Bloodhound MkI & II	Anti aircraft
Thunderbird	Anti aircraft
Red Top	Anti aircraft
Seaslug I	Anti aircraft
Malkara	Anti tank
Blue Steel	Airborne long range bomb
*Rapier	Anti aircraft
Ikara	Anti aircraft
Sea Dart	Anti aircraft
Seaslug II	Anti aircraft
Sea Wolf	Anti aircraft

Most of the above were defence oriented, plus space applications, like:

*Skylark	Atmospheric/astronomic research
Black Arrow	Satellite launcher
ELDO	Satellite launcher
*Falstaff	Upper atmosphere research

Those above with * are the ones which knew me well.

Their relative time scales are:
1953 to 1960   Bloodhound Mk I
1961 to 1965   Bloodhound Mk II
1965 to 1968   Rapier
1969 to 1978   Skylark

Other chronological indications appear where appropriate under the various subject headings, and the general flow of time is from the "Introduction" to the "Requiem".

The dedication is to the Skylark team which figuratively lit the blue touch paper and which had the overriding responsibility of making sure that each rocket left the launcher at the right time and in a fit condition.

The team members, a few more than a first eleven, were each congenial, competent, conscientious and cheerful — the vital four Cs for a successful combination. And who could ask for more? Most of us commuted from Adelaide to work at Woomera during trial periods, at other times doing planning and maintenance work at base at Salisbury, some 15 miles north of the city of Adelaide.

Many names from those now distant Bloodhound days still invoke strong and happy memories, names such as:

David Farrar, OBE	The brilliant Chief Designer
David Lloyd	Chief Aerodynamicist, new project leader and friend
Hugh Metcalfe, OBE	Aerodynamicist when first met, friend and subsequently a company Director
Doug Robertson	Bloodhound Project Engineer, yachtsman and stargazer

Alfred Oscar Henry Gale	Bloodhound Project Engineer and subsequently a company Senior Executive — the Gods always shone on AOHG
Philip Rosser	Friend, Aeronautical Engineer and Project Manager
Peter Windsor	Who found me the English boat.

Fathered by such people as those above, the Bloodhound Weapon System proved to be both a technical and financial success. It was bought as a defence system by several countries, including UK, Sweden, Switzerland and Australia, and has only recently been withdrawn from service in the UK.

On the Woomera front, mention must also be made of the Range men who sat in the hot seat, designated "CON ONE", Alan Mole, John Russell and Charles Pugsley. That position can best be likened to the conductor of the orchestra. It was the open face of the Range Authority and from that chair executive control of all integrated trial activities took place - from conducting practices to actual launches. This function, as the prelude to each firing, included the initiation of the master countdown clock which switched certain automatic functions, the end point of which was the arming of all firing circuits and the actual firing pulse.

These men were a credit to the organisation and dealt with their responsibilities in that difficult position with both humour and skill.

You are only ever as successful as the collective team, and reference must also be made of Jack Somerton and Betty Cook- Jack for his outstanding contributions to data collection and assessment, and Betty for her vital work in Skylark trials planning. Names, names, names, if only one could say them all.

Acknowledgements

1.   *Heroes in space, from Gagarin to Challenger*, by Peter Bond, 1987, published by Basil Blackwell Ltd, 108 Cowley Road, Oxford OX41JF, UK. Chronological references to Soviet and USA space flights.

2.   Defence Science and Technology Organisation, (DSTO), Salisbury, South Australia. Woomera photographs.

3   Department of Defence for photographs it provided, taken in the Woomera restricted area.

4.   This publication was supported by the South Australian Government through the Community History Fund of the History Trust of South Australia.

The launch of a Bloodhound surface to air guided missile from
the Woomera Range

Introduction

I graduated from Sydney Technical College, as it was then known, in 1951 with a Diploma in Aeronautical Engineering. At that time I was employed as a research assistant in the Aeronautics Department of Sydney University.

In early December, 1952, I ventured aboard the P&O one class ship the *Mooltan*, for what was then a £120 passage to England in a six berth cabin, the aim being to seek experience there in the aviation industry, and see a bit of the northern hemisphere — the latter being something of a custom at that time for young Australians.

Fortunately the famous Bristol Aeroplane Company provided me with that opportunity and I was employed, after a hiatus of two months of security checking, as an aerodynamicist in the company's guided weapons department. At that time the company was developing the design of a surface to air guided weapon called Bloodhound. All Bristol designs bore names beginning with the letter B, dating back even to Bristol Boxkite days.

Bloodhound was destined for subsequent R&D testing at the Woomera Rocket Range, some three or four years hence so, by a happy chance, I found work in an appropriate discipline with the prospect of returning to Australia, when the time came, to be involved in that Woomera activity. The following descriptions and incidents relate to one or two English experiences but mainly to life on the Woomera Range. The initial period was very much 'early post World War Two'. Germany had demonstrated the potential of rockets, everyone

Bristol Bloodhound

now had to have better ones, spies were everywhere, and England still had some forms of rationing and unrebuilt bomb sites.

With one or two possible exceptions, everything that follows is factual and stems from active and direct involvement in the events. The time scale is 1953 to 1978, the latter year representing the last significant British rocket launch from the Woomera Range, certainly by the author's company, and quite likely by anyone. It was a very exciting and interesting period, and the human aspects of rocket work deserve to be recorded as well as the technical.

So — minus three, minus two, minus one, off we go!

England arrival

The good ship *Mooltan* arrived at Tilbury dock in mid January 1953, in the middle of a winter which saw many locals turn up their toes and move to either celestial places or down below! The old ship was fog bound for a whole week in the Thames, for all the world like being lost in space except for the continual ringing of bells and hooting of foghorns from vessels brave enough to still carry on their business. The venerable *Mooltan* had completed its final voyage and after releasing its last packet of passengers on the dockside, she was scheduled to present herself at a breakers yard. Somehow it seemed that a similar fate awaited her crew, but that is another story.

Being surprised to note that the local population looked as cold as I felt, I resolved to buy a chocolate from a local sweet shop to stoke up the internal fires. I found a likely shop only to be stumped when asked by the shopkeeper, on being presented with a chocolate of my choice, "Where are your coupons, luv?" Chocolate would have to await the necessary paperwork!

The weather was such that having established a position with the Bristol Aeroplane Company, and being advised that some time would elapse before security clearance would allow work to begin, I decided to strategically move to the Riviera's relative warmth until cash or lack of it, decreed that imminent paid activity was essential. Fortunately, this decision coincided with the security clearance and I gladly began work with Bristol in March, 1953.

The company recommended a boarding house in which to drop anchor and a great experience of its own that turned out to be. Suffice to say that this antipodean inherited the north facing attic room, which managed to grow ice on the inside of its little windows and solidify the water in the wash bowl that was kindly set nearby on a convenient, if similarly refrigerated window sill.

The establishment, ruled over by a middle aged English lady, provided full board for something like four pounds sterling per week, and had a coterie of some five or six transient/semi permanent male lodgers. Although by this time I proudly had obtained a venerable Austin 12, 1936 vintage for my own use, one of my fellow boarders worked at the same place and offered transport in his superior vehicle until the new boy was familiar with the route to work.

It was something like three or four weeks before the route to work became obvious. The routine of a morning was to present at the car, whereupon the owner would scrape a six inch diameter hole in the ice encrusted windscreen, through which to see to be able to navigate. Meanwhile, his companion sat in the opaque glass side of the car. Homeward bound was similar. One's car being immovable in the company car park, with brakes frozen solid until a thaw set in was another learning experience for one who had never even seen snow before.

On my first day at Bristol, being walked around the site by way of indoctrination, I was fortunate to see the demise of that famous aeronautical adventure called the Bristol Brabazon — the enormous aircraft that was the precursor of today's Jumbos. There it stood in the enormous hangar built specifically to house it, while artisans gripping circular saws walked along its fuselage, literally cutting it up like a beached whale, the scream of saws sounding its plight.

Another early unusual experience arose one afternoon when word flashed around the office that one of the company's prototype Britannia aircraft had force landed on the mud flats of the Bristol Channel just north of work. Naturally one had to see this sight, and in company, just a few minutes north after work, there the poor thing could be viewed, slowly being drowned by the majestic Bristol Channel tide. One more beached whale, but this time one at the very start of its career. The forced landing, it was discovered later, was the result of a warning system rather than a real emergency, but warnings are there for a reason, and not be treated lightly.

In passing, you might ask why I should have finished up at Bristol? When I left my previous job at Sydney University, I was fortunate enough to be provided with a reference from the Professor of Aero Engineering, Prof. A.V. Stevens. He also advised me to see a certain Defence person when I arrived in London to sound out work options. I saw that gentleman and he told me of two firms looking for people of the likes of me, one firm being Saunders Roe on the Isle of Wight, and the other Bristol Aeroplane Co. on the river Avon.

Knowing about Bristol's seafaring past and its links with Stevenson's Treasure Island, and having sold my sailing boat to fund my passage to England, I reckoned Bristol must be an ideal place to also renew my sailing activities. So I chose Bristol as the first interview, not appreciating at the time that the Isle of Wight was the mecca of English yachting, and that the river Avon and the nearby Bristol Channel had mind boggling forty foot tides.

So I went to Bristol, had a five minute interview with David Farrar, who glanced at my reference and said words to the effect, "I think you'll do." And that was that!

Throwing stick

Quite soon after my starting work at Bristol, it could even have been the first day, Richard Cocke, a senior member of the staff and one of the company's first users of the rocket range, entered the design office carrying a strange object. This happened to be my, and my companions, first sight of a woomera.

He had just returned from a visit to South Australia and the Range and as a memento had brought back a genuine Aboriginal throwing stick. As most would know the Aborigines call it a woomera, and the rocket town itself was appropriately given the same name.

The exhibition by the woomera toting sponsor, as his duties were labelled, was appreciated by all, especially by me, who had to see his first woomera those 12,000 miles from both their homes.

The boomerang flight

My introduction to work in England was technically interesting and not without surprise.

Before rocket trial activities had gathered their momentum at Woomera, local experimental firings were taking place at Aberporth, a charming and peaceful coastal town in South Wales. Aberporth looked out upon the waters of the St.

Georges Channel which separated South Wales from the green fields of Ireland. The rockets launched there had not the range capability to hazard the shamrocks to the west and their flights inevitably ended by a splash in the salty water of the Channel, with subsequent new homes for the lobster population for which Aberporth was noted. Attempts at recovery had been tried, but proved difficult and expensive — a thing that the Woomera Range later demonstrated to be one of its major advantages.

Just before my arrival a company rocket, an unguided prototype of the Bloodhound, had been launched from the cliffs high above the Aberporth beach. Its intended ballistic trajectory meant that, just like a tossed stone, it should have travelled more or less straight ahead and plopped into the sea some miles off shore. But this one had a mind of its own. To the great consternation of its launch crew and the locals, it zoomed into cloud and soon after was seen to be heading back home — to impact in one of Aberporth's green fields, not that far from its launcher! Great was the confusion. Red faces all round.

The reason for this delinquent behaviour had to be found and quickly, so each member of the Aerodynamics Group was given a sample trajectory to calculate, each using slightly different stabilities, the aim being to determine why the beast had these unscheduled homing instincts. Thus the half dozen or so of us spent several hours of furious slide rule activity on our complicated sums.

It is worth remembering that all the design work on the U.K.'s first generation of surface to air guided weapons was done without the benefit of computers. Their emergence as tools was not to take place until about 1956, and even then not without difficult birth pangs. This engineer therefore can claim to have started his professional life B.C. — before computers!

The reason for the boomerang behaviour was found to be connected with yaw stability, modifications were made, and the tendency was eliminated.

Leave it to the young

An interesting thing about the team designing the weapon system was that the average age, as far as I could see, could not have been more than about twenty seven years. This probably was a measure of the state of the art, in that only recent graduates had the necessary grounding in supersonic theory to be able to cope with the entirely new problems involved.

Not so the chief designer, a man possibly in his early thirties, an engineer in the classic mould, with the ability to do back of an envelope sums. Sums which subsequently might take his team of engineers considerable time and effort to substantiate.

Author top right, next to him Hugh Metcalfe, second left Phil Rosser, next left David Lloyd. Top left Peter Windsor, middle left with glass in hand is Alan Brown. All men from Bloodhound MkI aerodynamics section.

He had, for example, opted for what is called a "twist steer" homing system, considering it the natural thing to do. (*See* Appendix 1 for explanation).

The section leaders of the team were all products of childhoods of England's war years. National Service had been nearly universal during their early manhood, and the highest rank some might have attained would have been corporal or sergeant. Later, in the passage of years and experience, some were to become company managers and directors, overseeing the work of retired admirals and generals in the company sales force.

It was probably ever thus, that the majority of the world's innovative design is achieved by those who don't believe it cannot be done, and therefore proceed to do it.

Being a lone Australian surrounded by bright contemporary English and Welsh engineers had its moments. Like early in the piece finding, surreptitiously placed on my desk, a book entitled, *Peoples of the World*. It was opened at a page bearing at the bottom the inscription, 'an Australian', and above that a photograph of an Aborigine in threatening pose, complete with woomera.

The French influence

Aerodynamic design is all about flowing curves. (See Appendix 2). The forces on a body, due to air rushing past, vary with lots of things, and it is the way of the world that nothing is straightforward. So it is with aerodynamic forces which vary in strange ways and never, or hardly ever, as Gilbert & Sullivan might say, in straight lines.

So aerodynamicists use things called French Curves, pure sexist denomination, to describe the shapely stencils they use to fit curves through graphed series of dots.

Rarely do sets of French Curves equate to each other — each manufacturer having its own special shapes. One team member in the Bristol aerodynamics department had an excellent set of such curves. We all borrowed them in our work, and Bloodhound aerodynamic design was absolutely the child of those curves, its characteristics being completely defined by sections of their voluptuous shapes. Unfortunately, near halfway through the design phase, the owner of the curves decided to migrate to America, and to add to our loss, because he was a good bloke, he took his French Curves with him.

As I said above, curves come in different families, each with subtle changes in shapes, no doubt in complete harmony with their namesakes. The result was that our new French Curves no longer quite fitted the design shapes then on paper, and subsequent updates of the missile's aerodynamics resulted in subtle changes in the perceived performance of the rocket!

I remember at an airport once, seeing a well built young lady wearing a tight fitting jumper, which had emblazoned in the vicinity of the twin peaks, "no two the same". That is precisely what I mean.

Although nothing to do with French curves, the same migrating engineer with north country fiscal genes in his make-up, decided as an investment to take an exotic car with him to the USA.

With very little funds at his disposal he ventured to London and, with what he had available, he purchased a Lagonda, one of those venerable sports machines with bonnets seeming to stretch to infinity in front of the windscreen. Thus with the promise of high returns to come, he proceeded to drive his investment from London to Bristol along the A4 highway. No motorways in those days.

Now Lagondas are rich man's cars, not to be trifled with by young engineers with small pockets. He discovered by the same token that his newly acquired bonanza was extremely thirsty!

After at least three stops at petrol stations to top-up dwindling supplies of fuel the last top-up, with no money left, was negotiated by the temporary deposit of his revered wrist watch.

We never learned whether it was worth all the trouble. Maybe he is still to be seen at NASA, with the now much older Lagonda still out there in the parking lot? Mind you, petrol is much cheaper in the USA, a Lagonda would go a lot further on a wrist watch's top-up!

Where are you now, Alan Brown?

Secret weapon

In the English county of Hampshire there is a famous aeronautical research place called The Royal Aircraft Establishment. Early in 1954 a small team of four of us from Bristol visited the RAE to carry out wind tunnel tests on an accurate scale model of the Bloodhound missile. At that time the RAE was one of the few sites in the world with the experimental luxury of a supersonic wind tunnel.

The metal model, only about twelve inches long, was housed for the trip in a beautifully polished wooden box. There were two reasons for the box — firstly the model had sharp bits in places, like the edges of its wings, and these had to be protected against possible damage, and secondly, a security classification banned unauthorised viewing of our little missile.

Nowhere in England, at least by Australian standards, is very far from anywhere else. We drove the odd seventy miles from Bristol, checked into a hotel not far from the RAE, and presented ourselves for security clearance and work.

The tests lasted about two weeks, with our model being blasted with winds of up to fourteen hundred miles per hour while all the necessary measurements were being taken. This data was all faithfully recorded on numerous sheets of paper, to be taken back to base for detailed analysis. It was a great treat for an Australian to be present on this hallowed ground, a historic aviation birthplace of many great achievements.

Our return home to Bristol by car, after finishing the tests, called for a lunch break en route, and a typical English roadside cafe was chosen at random as the watering hole. The team selected a table and drew up an additional chair for the shining box and its precious contents.

A waitress sidled up, and with a smile addressed the group, "What have you got there, luvs? A secret weapon?"

To which a chorus replied, "Yes!"

What else could you say?

Where am I?

In engineering in Bristol, and I am sure it is similar in many large organisations, it was easy to fall into the trap of becoming a 'meetings engineer'. There were in-house meetings and in-town meetings, one of which is mentioned later.

On the design side of Bloodhound I, there were several different sections. I was in the aerodynamics section, but there was a structures section, aeroelasticity section, control systems section, and probably others I have forgotten.

The section leader of the structures section was a clever man at his work, but known to be absentminded. This would explain why one day at work one of his section answered the phone, to find that it was his section leader calling from London.

"I'm here in London", he said breathlessly, "tell me, which meeting am I supposed to be at?"

Place of fire

During my first stint at Bristol, the company embarked upon the design of a recoverable supersonic target. This was based on the Bloodhound missile design to a large extent, including the thrust being provided by twin ramjet engines. (See Appendix 3). The overall shape therefore resembled that of Bloodhound to a marked degree but with the significant exception that its nose was a long spike. This spike was designed such that on completion of a mission, after parachute deployment, the inert rocket would spear into the ground using its mosquito-like proboscis.

Like Bloodhound, the machine had moving wings, and thus could be controlled from the ground by radio signals. At that time, in the mid 1950s, target aircraft were available like Meteors and Canberras for subsonic guided weapon testing, The Jindivik was on the horizon for high subsonic speeds, but

Bristol Bobbin, on trial at Woomera, showing its parachute recovery system

a dearth of targets existed in the supersonic region. Thus the Bristol design showed promise.

The company management decided that this rocket should have an Australian name, and knowing that they had in their midst a relatively tame Australian, I was delegated to obtain a selection of names from back home from which a choice could be made. Several books of Aboriginal words subsequently arrived in Bristol and the rocket was christened the Bristol Bobbin, maintaining, you will note, the tradition of names starting with B.

Sydney folk will be familiar with the pleasant place called Bobbin Head on one of the picturesque reaches of the beautiful Hawkesbury river. Not many would know however that to the Aborigines it denoted a "place of fire".

Bonkers

To give you an idea of the techniques used to have confidence in the aerodynamic design of a rocket, one such technique involved the use of things called bonkers.

A bonker was a small rocket motor, having a short duration, like seconds only, thrust period. One of these could be placed just aft of the rocket's centre of gravity, and during flight, when the bonker was ignited during flight it would cause the rocket to suddenly change its heading and then slowly, as the effect of the sudden thrust wore off, the rocket would return to its original heading.

These bonkers were most valuable in some stability calculations. (See Appendix 4).

Interesting things, bonkers, and not as silly as they sound.

Before Woomera

I spent some four years in Bristol as a member of the design team, gaining experience in the various aspects of the overall design. So when the time came to move camp to South Australia in 1956, I was qualified to carry out initial assessment of missile performance in trials undertaken at Woomera. This preliminary assessment was passed as quickly as possible to my masters in the U.K. so that they had reliable post trial information on which to plan imminent future trials, prior to their own receipt of hard technical data, such as telemetry records, trajectory and velocity information. (See Appendix 5 — Trials data).

Of course, life in England had many attractions other than the technical. My venerable, rusty 1936 Austin 12/4, which I'm told meant 12HP and four cylinders (and certainly the four cylinders were still there, but doubt remained about all of the twelve horses) carried me and friends about England and the continent and always got us home. One time, with my friend David Lloyd, the car took us to Lynmouth, a charming little town on the Somerset coast, descended to from the north by the steep Countesbury Hill. Now David Lloyd was not a small man, you meet him again in *Best Man*. In fact the return journey to Bristol, up the famous Countesbury Hill, was only achieved by David getting out of the car and meeting me at the top of the hill. Friendship overcomes such trials.

I also had the long term loan of an ancient, eighteen foot, gunther rigged sailing boat. In this in the summertime, I and friends explored the many sandbanks of Poole Harbour and beyond. If it was fine, we slept in the concave hull, if it rained, which was not unusual, we slept in the Railway Hotel by the dockside. In those days, only an Australian would drive all the way from Bristol to Poole, (perhaps 60 miles), each weekend in the summertime. Surely it was a once a year trip?

Of significance also is the fact that whilst in Bristol I was introduced to a school teacher named Ann, and when the time came for farewells to friends, the passage back to Australia in the white ship, *Orion*, saw us as relative newly weds on the high seas of adventure, casting off from the Tilbury dock in October 1956.

The time had come for Bristol to establish a base in South Australia from which to support its planned activities at Woomera. A retired English army officer, Colonel Jack Warner, was selected to manage the Australian Company, and with a staff of some forty personnel he established the Bristol Aeroplane Company, Australia, based in the Contractors Area of what was then known as WRE or The Weapons Research Establishment, Salisbury.

WRE, a Commonwealth of Australia organisation, was charged with the responsibility of organising and overseeing the operations of Woomera from a weapons trials point of view. WRE itself was housed in what had been a very dispersed munitions factory during WW2. Salisbury was some 15 miles from Adelaide, along what was then a quiet country road. The district around WRE was farming country, wheat on the plains and sheep in the adjacent hills.

Partnership arrangements between the UK and Australian Governments for the establishment of the Woomera Range and its supporting facilities were first agreed in 1947, and were renewed initially at 3 to 5 year intervals, the arrangement being known as the Joint Project. Woomera is north of Adelaide and in those days had something like 100,000 square miles of prohibited area.

By 1956 the facilities at the Woomera Range were quite well established, but more on that in the next chapters. During his pre-Australian settlement, Jack Warner had arranged with the South Australian Government that his trials team would be housed in the satellite and embryonic town of Elizabeth, adjacent to Salisbury and WRE. The town of Elizabeth was named after Queen Elizabeth II, and was expected to be a grand example of modern decentralisation.

The houses were all built by the South Australian Housing Trust, a Government body. So there we were, Bristol and Jack Warner's team, families, newly weds and singles, marshalled into modest new rental homes, with company-supplied basic furniture, and food in the fridge. All of us were new settlers in a town that would not celebrate its first birthday for several months, each house with virgin ground outside its four walls, no pathways or grass, the roads that existed then being dirt tracks which quickly became quagmires with light rain, and one local shopping centre, comprising something like four vital shops. The spirit of the newness and not quite isolation produced a bond between all of the 1956 colonists that remains today among the survivors of those early years.

The modus operandi of this Aussie Bristol establishment were as follows: the local group provided the nucleus of missile preparation and assessment teams. They would be topped up by visiting missile system technicians and what were called sponsors, men in charge of rocket firings at the Range. Rocket parts were sent from Bristol to be assembled and tested at Salisbury, then transported to Woomera by truck for retesting and launch.

Alf Gale, mentioned earlier and now deceased, was one of the first sponsors and project leaders. Alf was a remarkable person; had he lived a century or so before he would undoubtedly have been a doer and shaker on the high seas, or opened up new territory along the Zambezi. He had the way of getting the most out of those in his team, and he seemed to be almost always right in his decisions. Whether it was divine intervention or superior knowledge was not always obvious.

Doug Robertson, also one of the company's early project leaders, is another remembered face, almost the antithesis of

Alfred. Quietly spoken and sincere, Doug served in the army medical corps during WW2. His hobbies were sailing and astronomy, which separates activities nicely into daylight and night time affairs. He had his own self made sky-telescope mounted in his backyard in Klemzig, a suburb of Adelaide, and is the only person I have ever met whose living room ceiling carried images of the southern constellations. He now lives with wife Babs by the sea in Suffolk. They have a timeless cottage and salt water to sail on.

Woomera village

The first impression of the Woomera area, whether travelling by train, car or plane, is one of unbounded two-dimentional space. The Village, probably the only place called a village in the whole of Australia, and that no doubt owing to its then largely British commitments and staffing, sits like an oasis in the wilderness.

To travel in the area is for all the world like being in a ship at sea. All round is a clear, slightly undulating horizon, as seen from a ship in mid ocean.

The village itself, about half a mile square, is also like a ship at sea. If you don't like it, it is difficult to get off unless, particularly in the early days, you were prepared for the many dusty and corrugated miles of dirt track back to Port Augusta and civilisation beyond.

For some considerable time the village was run on strictly military lines. For transient visitors, typically transported by daily and elderly DC3s, there were several messes to which one was allocated, depending on rank. If one didn't possess a rank, then work status or salary was the determining factor. This system resulted in trials teams being divided between Senior Mess, Sergeants Mess and Junior Mess, which put

The 1956 Bristol Aeroplane Company — Australia Team. Author front row, 4th from right; Alf Gale front row 6th from right and Jack Warner front row 7th from right.

some egalitarian noses out of joint and did little to foster team spirit.

In the first few years the sleeping accommodation was in fibro huts, ovens in the summertime and igloos in winter, complete with hot and cold running ants.

One had to dress for dinner replete with tie, regardless of ambient temperature, in true upper lip style. The mess food was substantial and military, if not Cordon Bleu. Take it or leave it.

I still remember my very first meal. Sleeping and hidden from view within my well cooked mashed potato, lay the corpse of a mature but harmless cockroach.

Entertainment in this very monastic environment was limited. There was always the bar, and for those with sporting bent, either billiard tables, table tennis, darts, cards or books. Drinks were cheap, thus clearly the favourite pastime became steady drinking, with unsteady bouts with the rest, like the game of so called "Slosh", which was a version of billiards played without the use of cues, involving much running around the table before balls came to rest.

Once a week there was the diversion of the open air cinema. Its main attractions, at either of the two venues, were often the superb desert sky, with stars as bright as light bulbs, and the surprisingly frequent trail of shooting stars.

This state of affairs lasted until about 1970 by which time the ELDO (European Launcher Development Organisation) had ceased its launch programme at Woomera and its mess and accommodation buildings became available to those rocket teams which had hitherto looked upon that superior architecture with considerable envy.

The Village was not short of amenities. Adequate shops existed to satisfy the townfolks' needs, a swimming pool was there to quench the customary heat of the day and a beautiful green oasis of a sports field lay in the northern corner of the town. Schooling of course was available and it was acknowledged that the pupils there boasted an above average

The Senior Mess building in the foreground with Woomera Village houses in the background. Beyond is the featureless 'sea' of the desert.

IQ, probably due to the unusual social and educational standard of the Village inhabitants. It was not your standard country town.

Under canvas

I n the beginning at Woomera some of the military personnel had to rough it in tents. This must have been a most uncomfortable existence to put it mildly. As a consequence of this hardship, those living under such dire conditions were entitled to a 'living under canvas award'. So the story goes.

The growth of civilisation brought with it corrugated iron huts to replace the tents and engender a note of permanence.

The story also goes that it wasn't long before canvas was erected inside the tin dwellings, so that the inmates could still

claim the award and not suffer a loss in drink money. It's a good story, smacking of real Aussie ingenuity. Be nice if it was true.

The Range

Travel to the Range from the Village, a distance of some thirty odd miles, was undertaken early on by geriatric buses, vehicles that had been superannuated from city life and sent outback to see out their days in the sun. Some were magnificent articulated machines with upper decks. Later on, presumably as the old buses went to the great highway in the sky, the teams were provided with Commonwealth cars to travel in, less romantic but much more comfortable.

The bus trip was often a sobering journey. Here, at least, there was no discrimination by rank. Team leaders travelled side by side with folk of much lower station, difficult by standard of dress to tell apart, the latter at times probably appearing the more alert.

The long bitumen road, in 1956 probably the only bit of bitumen within one hundred miles, led eventually to the entrance to the Range. This was guarded by Commonwealth police to whom one had to wave one's security pass to gain admittance. The entrance gateway was on a small rise and once there the viewer could behold the Rangehead with its scatter of well separated buildings, consisting of Range Centre for executive Commonwealth staff, Instrumentation Building for trials control and data collection, Range Workshops, sundry large hangar like buildings for rocket preparation, launcher pads, launch control posts and bunkers for firing personnel, buildings for military staff, and in the distance, a fully equipped airfield for target aircraft operations.

The Range Centreline, the nominal direction for firing, extended roughly north west as an imaginary line across the continent to the coastline of Western Australia. Someone said once that this line was on the great circle route to Moscow. Probably an apocryphal tale rather than factual.

Station people, surprisingly, lived throughout the Range, gathering a livelihood from the sheeps' backs. The density of sheep per square mile is remarkably small, but as the square miles are many, so are the sheep. For safety reasons the authorities built shelters for the station families to repair to during firings, when it was deemed their location might be near an impact area. It is said that the station folk usually stayed outside to witness the fireworks rather than scuttle below, and preferred to grow mushrooms in their shelters instead.

Long observation suggests that the Woomera sheep graze with heads pointing westward in the mornings and eastwards in afternoon. They either prefer warm behinds or like to keep the sun out of their soft eyes when they eat.

Kangaroos abound in this part of the world. Their skill at maximising precious and elusive protection from the piercing rays of the sun is a credit to their species. In this region of almost nil shade that skill is a most useful characteristic. Humanity has brought with it such things as telegraph and power poles. Not, one would be forced to agree, particularly shade-inducing devices but the roos are clever. Thus it is common to see a family, grading from large to small, biggest near the pole and the rest in each others' shade, slowly circling the erection in phase with the movement of the sun. They liked to sit on the warm bitumen road, particularly at sunset, which might have given them a warm feeling in the stern, but did nothing to improve their life expectancy from passing cars.

Wedge tailed eagles controlled the skies, even at times causing some concern to helicopter pilots by invading their airspace, and being blessed with superior airworthiness. Their propensity for nesting in the telegraph poles proved a nuisance until special nesting structures were provided for them, suitably spaced from live wires.

These birds were large enough and tough enough to produce radar echoes, leading to tales of unidentified flying objects on radar screens. It is unlikely however that one was ever shot down by a missile in anger.

Emus strutted about the place in their superior fashion. If any animal gives the appearance of being well bred and haughty, it has to be this funny bird. Occasionally they created some confusion at the Village Airport by failing to give priority on the landing strip to machines which flew a little better than they did.

Firing rockets was good medicine for the human plumbing system. The excitement kept one regular. Or could it have been the drink? Anyway, to cater for last minute emergencies, launch areas were equipped with handy and very civilised outside dunnies, simple one or two holers complete with the luxury of flush toilets. One young visiting English engineer got more than he bargained for one day when he opened the door of one to relieve himself only to be brushed aside by a large, suddenly liberated grey kangaroo which had taken up unintended incarceration, albeit with drinking water supplied.

The Kooly mess

Just before the entrance to the Range stood the Kooly Mess. The original building resembled a wild west saloon in more ways than just its exterior appearance. It was a pretty rugged place in which to carouse. By the late '60s it was replaced with a hygienic looking cafeteria, picture cinema style in architecture, which provided meals for those who worked on the Range. As in the Village, the food was plentiful and military like, served by men with their hearts in the work. A colleague once enquired politely, and probably optimistically, if the advertised steak of the day was rump, and received the quaint reply, "… if you want arse, see Charlie!"

Kooly, short for Koolymilka, squatted beside a large salt pan, several square miles in area. This was known as Lake Koolymilka, despite the fact that for something like nine years out of ten it was drier than a lizard's tongue. A fascinating place. To walk onto the surface of the salt pan was to experience complete stunning silence. Better than any soundproof room ever invented. An eerie place.

Kooly boasted fairly basic huts for overnight sleeping by trials people should the exigencies of work call for such drastic measures, but it did have a memorial swimming pool, in which some memorable competitions were contested.

Kooly also was the site of what was euphemistically called The Works and Jerks camp. This had an appearance for all the world like a concentration camp, and it housed the largely migrant group of souls who carried out the labouring tasks in the Range area. It is doubtful if any Australian migrants ever served their Antipodean apprenticeship under more adverse circumstances. It appeared to be darker shades of the Foreign Legion. A visit to their weekly cinema night, organised by the humanity of the area padre, was always a night to remember. The whistles and hurrahs of the 'legionnaires' delight at the sight of the Betty Grables of this world was only interspersed by the accidental tinkle of broken bottles. Another rugged place!

By the side of the salt pan, shimmering in the relentless sun, was the Koolymilka football ground, complete with the mandatory four goal posts. Aussie Rules type, and little else.

One year there came the big wet, when the lake became full to its complete majesty and an ephemeral 'Kooly Yacht Club' was formed by residents in the Village. One brave soul towed his yacht up from Port Augusta behind his car and launched it in Lake Kooly, mooring it in a picturesque little bay by the Kooly mess. He claimed the worldly distinction of being the only yachtsman to have scored six points by sailing between the aforementioned goal posts.

One poor soul drowned in the lake. This must be one of the least of life's probabilities. The reader can be assured that this will never happen to him or her. More on the lake later.

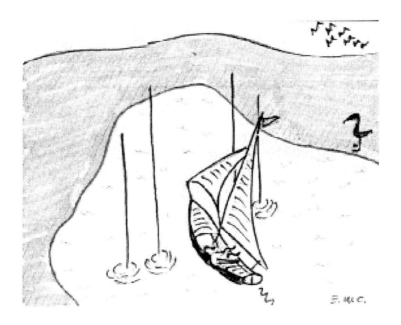

Rocket trials

Apart from those rockets designed and launched for purely scientific purposes, the likes of Skylarks and others which studied the atmosphere and stars and ionosphere, the objective of the main rocket activity, certainly up to the year 1975 or thereabouts, was to achieve accuracy in shooting down target aircraft. These generally unmanned aircraft were flown from the Range airstrip, Evetts, by skilled operators. Some manned aircraft trailed towed targets but these were relatively few. Of the unmanned target aircraft, there were many spectacular hits and misses. These aeroplanes were well utilised. Some were getting on in years, fragile, and something of a bother to maintain in flying condition — a situation which no doubt caused their ground staff to cross fingers and hope the next missile firing might take such a Meteor or Canberra off their lists forever!

Rockets were prepared for flight in the Test Shops, each allocated to a particular project. At one stage in Woomera's active existence there would have been no less than three surface to air guided missile projects in operation on the Range at the same period, each competing for the opportunity to fly.

When ready for flight the rockets were loaded onto their special launchers, then pre flight tested and fired according to well documented procedures. A tradition developed that when one's missile inadvertently happened to fail to destroy its target — not all that infrequent in the early days — one could claim in the mess that night that the 'Miss Distance Pot' had been set for just such a result. The design of imaginative Miss Distance Pots reached a high degree of precision!

It should be understood that early missiles were not in fact expected to actually hit the target but were designed to get close enough to be within range of their warheads. Later, smaller missiles were developed to actually hit the target, which led to them becoming known as 'hittiles', but this was a non serious appellation.

One of the interesting nuances of shooting down a target was the inevitable result that very soon afterwards a team of accident investigation experts would arrive from Melbourne, to determine why the aircraft crashed. As though it was by accident rather than design! In fact their visits were very welcome and their expertise often proved vital in determining where the target had suffered its mortal damage. There was at least one case where a target was caused to crash because the missile was under so much stress when it went past that it broke up, and pieces damaged the target sufficiently to cause its demise.

Rocket launches were programmed with the Range Authority, Australian Government personnel whose responsibility it was to schedule Range operations between the various Range Users. The latter were usually English companies with U.K. Government contracts to develop weapon systems, although mingled with these was a smattering of local trials activity also.

The pace of development and enthusiasm of the trials teams was such that in the early hectic years, the bidding for Launch Slots, as they were called, was full of rivalry. If someone missed a slot due to unreadiness there were always others eager to bid for the vacant launch opportunity. The complexity of the systems was such that many things could go wrong during the last few minutes and thus abort a trial. When you consider that the probability of a complete system being 'go' is the product of the probabilities of all its component parts, you begin to understand the chances. So, if there are three vital parts of a system and each has a ninety percent chance of working, then the combined probability of being ready descends to about seventy three percent. And there are many more than three components in a weapon system. Stated like that, it's a wonder any of them work.

Weapon systems were always a mix of contracted parties, like propulsion system, guidance system, control system, and so on, and any one of these could suffer problems in the run down to launch. Additionally the Range Authority equipment such as radar, telemetry, doppler and the many Range cameras could all have hiccups. Not to mention weather. This often led to a 'chicken' type situation, where, if the fault was in one's own system, one delayed to the very last moment before crying STOP, in the hope that someone else had a problem and would take stop action first. It was an embarrassment to stop a trial, but when you did, it was interesting to see others suddenly finding things to do on their equipment.

There were complicated options one had in delaying a launch. Words like cancellation, withdrawal, hold, stop and abort were used, each defining how close to launch time one chose to pull out. Up to a certain time in a launch sequence one could request a HOLD, hopefully giving one time to remedy a minor problem. If the time in the countdown went beyond that for which a hold applied, then one could take STOP action, by calling 'stop' over the intercom network, whereupon the launch controller in the Instrumentation Building, the man in charge of all range integration, and firing circuits in particular, would stop the clock. Alternatively one could push one's own stop button and achieve the same result. All a matter of timing.

One unfortunate use of such a stop button occurred once when a missile caught fire on its launcher during a launch sequence. The button, as well as stopping the firing, also automatically switched off all the Range cameras, in particular those trained upon the burning missile. This meant that vital optical evidence as to the cause of the conflagration was lost. Our John Thomas was brave or rash enough to peep over the nearby blast wall, and proved to be the only eye witness. The fire not only destroyed the missile but also its launcher — it was a case of where it would have been better probably to let her fly.

The authorities operated what was called a Clean Range Policy. After all the bits had returned to earth after a firing, a RECOVERY TEAM would go out and collect everything from the impact site and return them to the contractor, crunched as they well may have been. Hitting the solid Woomera dirt at supersonic speed does amazing things to what previously were elegant shapes. Sometimes the contortions proved to be even more elegant, artistically if not functionally.

This clean range policy was vital in finding one's bits quickly and not having to pore over other remnants which otherwise may have been there to confuse the matter.

The recovery aspect of the Woomera Range was one of its major benefits and always was a source of important information. If something had gone wrong it was amazing, with skilled detection work, what could be gleaned from diligent examination of the wreckage. The recovery team took great pride in their work, always on their mettle to find things quickly, as almost a matter of honour.

Woomera in its heyday was a very busy place, and occupied the attentions of many people. In 1971 for example, probably well after the salad days, the total WRE staff at base in Salisbury would have been over 1,300 and the staff at Woomera about 900.

Things ain't what they seem!

Rockets were tracked by sophisticated means, primarily by radar, of which the Range boasted several. Immediately after launch the Recovery Team could receive impact coordinates downrange, sometimes measured in hundred miles plus, and head for the site expecting to find what they were looking for. If they found themselves on the wrong side of a fence which stretched for miles, it could mean a hefty detour or fence rebuilding, neither welcome options.

Mapping anomalies came to light under these circumstances when the impact point plotted on the map showed a fence to be on the wrong side of the wreckage.

Since the fences only subdivided station property there was no question of property rights, only confusion to the recovery party.

Local bushmen at times were a great help in finding the bits. It was not unusual to come across some workers out in the wild, miles from anywhere, to be given the useful information, "We heard a noise, over there."

The grand tradition of recovery was begun by the inimitable Percy Hawkins and continued later by Don Tungate and his team.

The motherly approach - Bloodhound

There's a saying that art and fiction, or something similar, imitates life. So also does engineering. The team had one rocket series in which the launch of a rocket very closely emulated the birth of a child. Everyone is familiar with the use of the word umbilical to describe the ground to rocket link while the rocket is on its launcher. In this particular case the launcher was truly the missile's mother. Before launch, the vital hydraulic fluid needed by the missile was supplied to it from the launcher via a thing called familiarly 'the donkey's plonk'. It had that look about it. The mother launcher supplied the rocket's bloodstream, albeit hydraulic oil.

Upon launch the rocket severed this bloodline connection, with non return valves inhibiting any blood (oil) loss, and as the rocket went off on a life of its own its own heart, or pressure vessels, took over and supplied the vital fluid flow.

Each launch was another birth for the launcher, attended by pre and post natal engineers.

The joys of travel

M ost trials personnel commuted to Woomera by air from Adelaide on a weekly basis. Over the years these travellers saw the history of aviation unfold around their seats. Travel commenced in the already venerable DC3s and graduated via Convair to Fokker Friendship. Later, as passenger lists declined in numbers, resort was made to light aircraft, which heightened the feelings either of adventure or dread, depending upon the attitude one adopted to aviation.

In the middle years when hijacking was in vogue overseas, it always struck the captive Woomera bound fliers as slightly odd that they were subjected to the same baggage checks as those destined for more exotic ports of call. A hijacking to somewhere like Kangaroo Island would have been a welcome diversion.

With such a seasoned bunch of air travellers these to and fro Woomera flights often proved entertaining; everyone knew each other, whether from the same team or rival camps, and hostesses were on first name terms, friendly but not familiar.

In the DC3 days of the fifties several groups of individuals would play games with the pilots by lurching en masse up and down the aisle, thus causing the pilot to continually have to retrim his controls. Until he tired of the sport and threatened to drop a few off.

Valium in the form of alcohol was the antidote some used to keep their feet on the ground. There were some interesting flights. Difficult DC3 weather was heralded by the not unusual black banks of cumulus which sometimes blocked one's path. One flight across Spencer Gulf was noteworthy, with the aircraft flying so low to avoid the cloud base that squalls could be seen sweeping across the waves beneath the plane.

To add to the feeling of all friends together, the pilots on some flights would leave their cabin door open so that those up the tube could see through the front windows. Generally all that could be seen was blue skies of course. In winter though one could often watch in terror as ice slowly enveloped the windscreen and one wondered whether the blokes in front really knew where they were or where they were going. It was always a great relief to see the stuff melt away when the plane descended for landing.

The hostesses must have had an interesting life on these bush excursions. One told of one flight when she noticed a small boy looking under his seat with great consternation. When she asked him what his trouble was, he replied, "Please miss, I've lost me snake".

Travelling slowly

Mention has been made elsewhere of travelling between U.K. and Australia by courtesy of the RAF Transport Command. Not being of a commercial nature, should the aircraft become unserviceable for any reason it was not always possible to obtain spare parts quickly. The record flight for longevity between England and Australia during the Woomera years was twenty three days from start to finish. A series of delayed departures between U.K. and Ceylon, as it was then known, caused some of the passengers to have financial problems. Before leaving for Singapore more shopping money had to be remitted to them to carry on as they had originally planned.

On the subject of shopping, Changi Village in Singapore was the most favoured destination. In those days the Village consisted of a string of tempting shops on either side of the road, offering wares at prices unheard of at home bases, even before haggling over what one was prepared to pay ever commenced. The RAF mess was sited near to where the little village shopping centre was, just a short walk away, and one of the pleasures of the whole flight was to wander through the shops, being greeted as long lost friends by the traders; offered Coke to drink and remarkable bargains. Trade was ever brisk.

"Do you know Mr So-and-So?" they would ask, mentioning the name of a colleague, "Good customer, Mr So-and-So!"

A friend and colleague, Jack Somerton, now no longer with us, clearly had left an impression in Changi. I, myself, witnessed the refrain, "Do you know Mr Somerton? Good customer, Mr Somerton!" Jack happened to have been one of the above slow motion Transport Command flight passengers; maybe he had more time to become well acquainted with such vendors?

Loose talk

It was common knowledge, in fact trials personnel were constantly reminded, that telephone conversations over the private lines between Woomera and Adelaide were monitored, to inhibit talk on matters with security sensitivity or to deal with those who ignored the rule.

It was therefore no surprise to be confronted one day during Bloodhound I trials in 1957 by a gentleman from Security. He had with him a transcript of a recent phone conversation I had had with a radar colleague at the Range. The security man handed me the transcript and asked that I confirm it to be a fair record of our chat. It was, of course. A telephone conversation in black and white is an interesting and unusual bit of literature!

For some time interference problems had been degrading our radar data, not seriously but something that could be done without, and work was going on to eliminate it. The caller had remarked, and there it was on paper: "We've got that noise back again. It must be the Russians, ha, ha, ha".

The security man wished politely to be convinced that Boris was not really spoiling the game, and hopefully he left assured this was so. Clearly it was one of those calls that had to be investigated. The eight letter word, "Russians", was henceforth struck from our discussions!

No soup thanks

For some time after the commencement of trials work at Woomera, the RAF Transport Command operated a weekly shuttle service between England and Edinburgh Airfield, the latter being an air force base near the WRE at Salisbury. These aircraft carried personnel and equipment associated with the Joint Project work at Woomera.

Travel by this method was a delight. None of the now endless marathon hours spent throbbing on to reach unappealing airports seen only through blurred eyes and felt by numb extremities. Those were the days when the British Raj still had influence in the Middle East. Each night we spent the dark hours on terra firma, cossetted in one of the RAF bases which were once scattered like pearls across the world. Magic names like Changi, Colombo, Katenika, Tripoli, Ben Adam, Ghan and Nicosia, to name but a few. The flying was done in exotic aircraft, such as the Comet II.

One overnight stop, I well recall, at Aden was memorable. The passengers, suitably hungry after the flight from Singapore, presented themselves for dinner in the mess dining room. This room was particularly hot and humid, the atmosphere worsened by the proximity of the kitchen. The local Arab waiters, proud and keen to impress, began to serve the soup course and were bewildered by the distinct lack of interest in their offerings. What they seemed not to notice was that as they carried the hot bowls to the tables, sweat was falling in droplets from their grey chins into the plates. Outside, goat men tended their small flocks under the windows.

Karachi, and its Min Wallas hotel was another place to remember. This was another overnight stop to cherish in a funny sort of way. From the windows of this then version of Eastern opulence, the locals in their off white garb could be seen carrying out their business, and toilet, in the sand. The RAF flight crew advised, with genuine concern, that teeth cleaning in this part of the world was best left undone, that is unless one used whisky rather than the local water.

Changi has been mentioned before. During WW2 it was the site of the monstrous prison camp in which Allied soldiers were so grossly mistreated. In the '50s and '60s it was a placid Singaporean backwater. Nowadays it is the site of the bustling main Singapore airport but, when we knew it, it was the jewel in the crown of the Transport Command itinerary.

There is no doubt that Changi was the preferred stopover place. The shopping, as stated before, was legendary, the RAF barracks were comfortable and the food good. If the RAF had an ailing aircraft, if humanly possible it would be nursed to Changi airstrip for any repairs to be effected.

The shopping there was so popular that there seemed no limit to what one might buy and lug on board. Like large wicker baskets, crates of Noritaki china, radios and the host of other items bought at bargain basement prices. On one flight I was on, the RAF pilot, noting the numerous passengers struggling on board with their booty, demanded all and their purchases off the aircraft so that they might be weighed. He needed to be confident that takeoff could still safely be achieved!

The food on these flights consisted of cold collations in cardboard boxes, prepared at the various ports of call. The boxes tended to be returned a little heavier as each flight progressed, as the novelty of hard boiled eggs, etc., slowly wore off. The flights were also teetotal, which probably gave some hard bitten passengers a rest cure, and the seats, by RAF policy, were rearward facing, which gave a new dimension to air travel.

Ghan, a little speck of an island in the Maldive Group in the Indian Ocean just south of the equator, was another unique stopover point. Devoid then of any female population, probably by RAF regulation, it was said to be the shortest posting for British service personnel, no doubt for that reason. Certainly when an aircraft arrived with female passengers on board the welcoming committee was large, attentive and appreciative.

This generally very agreeable mode of transport continued between UK and Australia until about 1975. We civilians who had the pleasure of being thus cosseted by courtesy of the RAF were given arbitrary rankings for the duration of each flight. The peak of my assumed 'service career' was thus squadron leader, for one trip from England to Singapore, where incidentally this made me the highest ranking 'officer' on board and entitled me to be first on and first off! Such is fame.

Impact points

S trict safety rules applied on the Range. At all times safety was the order of the day. One thinks of a rocket range as being an inhospitable tract of semi desert unlikely to attract habitation, and free from signs of humanity, a place good only for throwing things up in the air and finding them when they fall. Superficially this was true, but it was rare to venture any distance downrange without seeing man tracks, discarded cigarette packs, or the ubiquitous empty Coke can. The climate is such that, most of the time, like an open tomb, disintegration and corrosion take a long time to proceed.

The rules of the firing game required that impacts could not be planned within a five mile radius of an inhabited place. There were other rules of course, like staying within the Range boundaries, but that was a critical one as far as planned impact was concerned. Now it happened that when circles of that radius were drawn around all possible centres of habitation, relatively small available impact areas remained. Or so it seemed. Taboo areas were homesteads, dams, shearing sheds, crutching sheds and other pastoral sites, and they were numerous.

The fact that one variety of rocket had a likelihood of impacting anywhere within a radius of some twenty miles from its aiming point seems at odds with the above, but to have had a "peopled" place as a planned impact point, and against all odds to have managed to hit it, would have looked a bit silly indeed. Hence the provision of shelters.

Undoubtedly the safest place to have been for any trial would be the nominated impact point, because it remained unscathed. But that would have been tempting Providence.

The aborted mission

New project trials were initiated at Woomera by the arrival at Weapons Research Establishment at Salisbury of a Planning Team from the company or companies involved in the project. Prior to the arrival of such teams some initial negotiations had been completed to ensure that in principle a new project was within the scope of the Range and its supporting facilities, for example data reduction, at Salisbury.

The planning team would introduce a phased trials plan for discussion with the Range Authority and, if accepted, the next stage of trials planning would carry on from there. All rockets, etc., launched at Woomera had to go through this preliminary acceptance procedure.

In the early 1960s a planning team set out from U.K. to introduce a new large rocket project to the Australian authorities, the team being led by a senior managing engineer from Bristol. In those days, as mentioned elsewhere, air travel on Woomera related topics was largely supplied by the United Kingdom by way of Royal Air Force Transport Command aircraft, initially in already antiquated Hastings aircraft and later by De Havilland Comet II jets. Such flights typically had a duration, England to Adelaide, of just under a week.

During the flight, and unbeknown to the Planning Team, the new project was debated at length in the British parliament, and given the thumbs down. The project was cancelled. To the mortification of the planning team, on its arrival in Australia, it learnt that all it had achieved was an expenses paid visit to South Australia and an empty-handed return to U.K.

The project that aborted would have been christened "Blue Envoy", and the managing engineer was a well known Bristol identity, Dennis Corrick.

Regimentally dressed

In 1961 my wife Ann and I armed, if that's the right word, with our then two children, returned to Bristol for about a year of updating on Bloodhound MkII. It was a pleasant year. The children's English grandparents got to know them, we renewed all of our old friendships and made some new ones.

One of the new ones was a retired English army colonel, name of Vernon Seal, now alas no longer with us. Vernon was the epitome of the English officer, in a nice sort of way. He was charming and always the gentleman. You knew by the sound of his stride that it was he when he approached along a corridor. His tennis was superior to mine (which I confess is no great recommendation) and he was always correctly dressed.

Vernon and I were required to attend a formal meeting at the Ministry of Defence in London to discuss Bloodhound II matters, and we got together to sort out travelling arrangements.

"By the way, Ted", asked Vernon, "will you be wearing your hat?" What does he mean, I thought, and then I realised what he wanted to know was, would I be wearing a bowler hat.

I confess I had to disabuse him by saying that my only hat was a white floppy one, probably not very suitable for MOD type meetings!

It was the same year, 1961 on the twelfth of April, that Yuri Gagarin became the first spaceman and cosmonaut, and the world would never be quite the same again.

Before Poseidon

Rocket firings normally took place off launchers fastened securely to a concrete base, more or less permanent installations. The designers of our weapon system decided to try using a more mobile system where the launcher base, rather than set in concrete, was placed on a steel mat pinned to the local ground. The blast of very hot and very fast efflux from rocket motors at the instant of launch can even erode concrete, depending on how perpendicular to the concrete the blast arrives, and therefore it was of great interest to know how many firings could take place from a launcher set on a blast mat on the ground, before a hole big enough to fall into was blown out.

To determine the extent of earth movement due to the blast, the launcher team, equipped with red paint and paint brushes, spent some time painting a good selection of the adjacent gibbers. An unlikely task for rocket engineers, but it proved valuable in defining the radius of the blast area.

The designers in U.K. also asked for samples of the ground surface, so spades replaced brushes and representative bits of dirt were sent off for analysis — maybe the first bits of virgin desert soil to be exported for non commercial purpose.

The launch experiments were successfully completed, and in the fullness of time advice arrived from U.K. which among other things included the comment, "We are surprised at the amount of nickel in the samples".

In retrospect, the team could well have started its own nickel boom, well in advance of the subsequent Poseidon adventure. No doubt the whole area is mineral rich, as events at Roxby Downs have since proved.

Collision course

My wife's parents were keen race goers. They also had two cars, one a chauffeur driven Bentley and the other a modest Morris Minor shooting brake. It's not that they were rich, but they made the most of what they had. For some reason I was never given the opportunity to drive the Bentley, it was the province only of the chauffeur, called Merry, no doubt because his surname was England.

On one of my not infrequent trips on business back to base in Bristol by courtesy of the RAF Transport Command, this time sans family, it was decided that Ann's parents, her sister and I would attend Royal Ascot. Four in the Bentley was deemed something of a crush, so we divided, father-in-law in the Bentley, and mother-in-law, sister Shirley and I, in the Morris. Father-in- law, sitting beside old Merry in the front seat of the Bentley, looked rather regal and lonely, but that's how we went, Morris in my capable hands.

The racing was entertaining, as was the audience. I remember bumping into the senior inspector and quality chief of Bristol Guided Weapons Division in the milling crowd of the members' stand, which clearly caused him some astonishment. Another of life's coincidences.

Came the time to depart. We walked to the members' car park, took up our positions as before, and set off on the green grass to the way out, the Bentley some thirty yards to the right of the Morris. I looked across to the Bentley to see which exit Merry had in mind, father-in-law waved energetically, and bang! there we had a gleaming new, chauffeur driven Bentley impaled on the front of the Morris.

The elegant owner of our prey and his good wife were sitting in the back of their car and gave every indication of being rather annoyed. Their chauffeur looked nonplussed as, no doubt, did I.

Owing to our small relative speeds the damage was slight. A modest dent in the right hand rear mudguard of the Bentley, and no discernible scratch on the mighty Minor. The owner of the dented mudguard, however, removed himself from his car, and was clearly irate. "That was a most diabolic thing you did, young man!" he said. I believe it was the first time I had ever heard the word "diabolic" used in conversation.

The upshot was that we exchanged names and addresses, he being Sir Edgar Young and I being Ted Chambers. The episode cost me one hundred English pounds to remove the blemish from the Bentley mudguard, thus preserving my father in law's no claim bonus. It also cost me some embarrassment!

Mind you, I was most careful when speaking to Sir Edgar, that no mention was made of me being employed in the guided missile business.

A bit of black paint

Part of the instrumentation available to missile and rocket companies was a Department designed camera system which could be mounted within the skin of the rocket, requiring an absolute minimum of space, and which would provide a series of photographs of, amongst other things, the earth's horizon. Quite often knowing the roll angle, for instance, of a rocket was a most vital piece of system information and such pictures were a source of this data.

Sometimes though, under certain meteorological conditions, the horizon that appeared on these photographs was too hazy and indistinct to be of use as the resulting accuracy would be too low.

In the team's less serious moments it considered requesting that the range Authority paint a broad black line around the

horizon thereby increasing the contrast in that region. For some reason the request was never officially forwarded.

Acceptance trials

An important part of Woomera's raison d'être was the carrying out of Acceptance Trials. It will be understood that the prime intention of companies' interest in designing and developing rockets as military hardware was the aim in the end that they would be purchased by governments as part of their country's defence systems. To this end, governments initially funded the early phases and when the time was deemed right, the Army, Navy or Air Force would supply personnel to operate the weapon system and carry out a scientifically designed set of trials to establish to its own satisfaction that the system met the forces' needs and specifications.

Also, as part of this procedure, the Weapons Research Establishment provided scientific officers to assist in the evaluation of these trials and in addition the Establishment provided staff, at least in the Bloodhound case, to set up elaborate mathematical models capable of simulating the missile performance throughout its range of performance. Such models could be used to test missile performance on the boundaries of its operational limits without the expense of actually firing and therefore using rockets. At one stage WRE, to its credit, probably had the most sophisticated analogue mathematical model of a weapon system in the world. It was called "AGWAC".

A small team of scientists operated this model, which occupied a large room or two of complex equipment, and proceeded to carry out a set programme of tests aimed at validating both the model and the system performance. It was not long before the team discovered that their model could handle the workload better than they could, and in the interests of physical wellbeing the decision was made that work would continue at the rate the humans could stand, rather than the machine.

The author was directly involved in no less than three sets of Acceptance Trials, these trials being carried out by services teams called JSTUs (Joint Services Trials Units).

Bloodhound I Acceptance took place in 1960, Bloodhound II in 1965, and Rapier in 1968. They were days of considerable launch activity, and no doubt executive stress.

I recall meeting the commanding officer of one JSTU, Wing Commander Mike Adderley of the RAF, in our local Elizabeth petrol station one Saturday morning, and he being moved to say something like, "God, Ted, a man should be paid double time to be home at weekends". Knowing that he had a goodly ration of children, I knew exactly what he meant.

It was then the golden days of rocketry. On the other side of the world major strides were being taken, and in 1969 the moon experienced its first human footsteps!

Towards the end of the series of simulator runs mentioned above, investigating the overall performance of the Bloodhound System, a small group of us from WRE and Bristol had a pleasant celebratory dinner in one of Adelaide's esteemed seafood restaurants. To mark the occasion we decided that it would be nice to establish a special society. Something with significant historical precedence. Someone suggested as a likely name, that of "The Society For The Conservation Of Angular Momentum". This was unanimously adopted, with the proviso that the word "Royal" should be included, and hence the society became known as "SCRAM".

Eyes off 1

It was during one series of Bloodhound Acceptance trails that I had the pleasure of sharing an office with Albert Dodd, the technical representative of a collaborating company in Bloodhound system design. It was our responsibility to provide the JSTU officer in technical charge with assistance in assessment of trials results.

Albert spent some considerable time in writing up details of the performance of a particular part of his bit of electronic wizardry. When the report was completed he passed it on to a higher authority for checking, and he learned a lesson in the ways of security!

To his great surprise the document was immediately classified at a level greater than the one he enjoyed and he was subsequently refused access to it.

Strange thing at times, security.

It's a boy

There was a constant flow of correspondence during trials, between Australia and England, and vice versa, some classified and some unclassified.

To maintain integrity it was important that the content of messages was confined to matters of business.

As the trials teams were composed of staff largely of inherent fatherhood age, some cryptic signals were sent occasionally to U.K. friends and colleagues to announce happy events.

One such telex, suitably unclassified, was sent advising the arrival of an offspring along the lines — "Pleased to report Smith System, mark two, arrived safely, with probe attached".

Best man

Bristol Aeroplane Company, through its various name changes due to different mergers and associations over the years from 1965 to 1970, remained at heart the friendly and paternalistic company that I had joined in 1953.

As an aside, there was a time not so long ago, when there was an English society called SBAC, which stood for the Society of British Aircraft Constructors. By the 1970s people were interpreting SBAC as the Society of Both Aircraft Constructors — such was the dropout and merger situation. Bristol, however stayed in the game, albeit finally becoming part of what is now called British Aerospace.

I have mentioned my friend David Lloyd before. When I first met him he was a Doctor of Philosophy in mathematics, chief aerodynamicist, a staunch Welshman to his bootlaces, and a somewhat quiet person, to boot. A gentle giant.

The time happily came when he and his fiancé, who was employed in London by the Royal Navy, chose a date for their wedding.

I had the honour to be invited to be best man at the wedding in London, some 12,000 miles away. Wheels were therefore put in motion and it was by pleasant coincidence that at the time of the nuptials I was asked to be undertaking a technical visit to the parent company.

And that is what happened. It was a grand affair. The Navy was represented and I hired a suit for the occasion. Christmas cards are still swapped each year to the happy couple, and several others who were met those many years ago.

Rapier

In mid 1965, with Bloodhound Mk II acceptance trials completed, my family moved to Stevenage, Hertfordshire, not far from London. I was to be indoctrinated into the ins and outs of the Rapier weapon system, which at that time was entering its final design phase, the intention being for me to have a role in the system's proving and subsequent acceptance trials at Woomera. As well as being technically interesting, this move provided my wife's parents with the pleasant opportunity to scrutinise their then three grandchildren once more.

The new generation of surface to air guided weapons by this time were evolving into smaller, more cost effective devices, and had new generation electronics to call upon. Rapier, unlike Bloodhound, was designed to be a "hittile", that is it had to actually strike its target to be effective. Its course to its chosen target was controlled manually by a soldier with a visual display of his missile and the target, and a small joystick with which to steer his missile, like a modern amusement arcade game of dexterity.

We returned to Adelaide in 1967, my task being to manage the installation of the Rapier weapon system, launcher and control cabin, on their allocated site on the Range. By mid 1968 this work had progressed sufficiently for the British army to have day to day control of the system and to bring it up to acceptance condition, the trials of which continued for some time.

Readers may know that Rapier was subsequently an active participant in the Falkland Islands war. The system was also purchased by the Australian Government.

In the northern hemisphere, the Russians had embarked upon their Soyuz spacecraft missions, and the United States had begun their famous Apollo launches.

Old faithful

Everyone with any involvement with the Woomera Range would have been aware that from February 1957, a rocket called Skylark had been using Range time and providing a spectacle to other range users, by its near vertical climb from its strange "meccano" looking launcher. And to continue that climb into the usual Woomera, clear blue sky, until it vanished from sight.

Up until the end of 1968 those launches had been the responsibility of WRE personnel. Skylark proved to be a popular research instrument for mainly United Kingdom universities and research institutions. By the end of 1967 more than 150 had been launched and when the curtain fell on Woomera that total had exceeded 250. I have a tie I wear with pride, which has inscribed on it, "SKYLARK 400", indicating that when the tie was made, about 1980, that 400 of the Skylark family had been launched worldwide.

At the end of 1968 our company obtained the contract to launch Skylark, and a brief indoctrination period took place for our company team to take over the reins from Skylark's then parents within the Research Vehicles Group of WRE's Aerodynamics Division.

The launch of a Skylark high altitude sounding rocket from its
30m (100ft) Woomera launcher

I had the dubious honour of being given the task of being the company's first OISC, Officer in Scientific Charge, of subsequent firings after the hand-over, but first, as part of the experience exchange, I was invited by the WRE team to join them in the launch bunker, to witness launch procedures and an actual launch. It proved to be a day to remember.

I witnessed the operations of the "wind monitor", whose duty it was to receive wind data from the met. people and plot these on a special chart, thus to obtain the correct launcher training angles, and so ensure the rocket went somewhere near its required impact point. I watched the operations of the "priming monitor", whose task it was to sit at a control console with many switches and dials, to carry out switching functions at the request of final preparation staff on the launcher, then when the launcher was cleared for action, to oversee the semi-automatic twenty minute launch sequence, ensuring that all the required switching events took place at the right time.

I shared the excitement of the experimenters, whose experiment sat in the nose of the rocket, upon which one of them may have a potential PhD hanging, and as the seconds ticked by noting the air of expectancy slowly rising in temperature.

I noted the WRE, OISC checking the wind monitor's progress, and passing and receiving information from "CON1", the Range Authority's man in overall control of the launch.

I heard the great roar as zero time arrived, and the boost motor lit up and the mass of the rocket zoomed upwards, all faces in the launch bunker intent on their instruments.

We all heard CON1 say, "All personnel to remain under cover! The rocket has broken up overhead, and pieces are falling on the launcher area. Stay under cover until we advise you."

I must say, apart from it being an interesting indoctrination, old Skylark was never quite so expansive again! Maybe it was just her way of closing a chapter in a very dramatic way?

Ten pin bowling

Skylark was a friendly rocket. To start with it had no intention of shooting down targets from the Woomera sky. One commentator once described its firings as "pedestrian", but to be present at the launch of any rocket and experience the excitement, and to learn later of the value of the experimental data, is anything but pedestrian.

A requirement arose, when our group in early 1969 took over the responsibility for such launches, to have available for trial planning purpose a solid sphere about nine inches in diameter. Launching against celestial objects, it was most useful to be able to plot the relative positions of such target stars on a celestial sphere whose centre represented Woomera.

Someone suggested that a ten pin bowling ball might suffice as our sphere, and it transpired on investigation that such balls are manufactured to very close tolerances, ideally suited for star plotting. The manager of a local Adelaide bowling alley was approached, and when he learned of the intention he was delighted to help, and donated two balls without finger holes, gratis.

These proved admirable for the job. Our machine shop carefully engraved lines of latitude and longitude, thus transforming the ten pin bowling balls into celestial spheres, and ten pin bowling moved into the space age!

All aboard the Skylark

(See Appendix 7).

This rocket was used almost exclusively for scientific research of the earth's upper atmosphere and astronomical investigations. It had been developed by the Space Department of the Royal Aircraft Establishment, Farnborough, and first flown in February 1957 as the U.K. contribution to the then International Geophysical Year activities. Well over four hundred Skylark firings have since taken place from various sites in the world, but predominantly from Woomera.

The rocket developed through various stages, culminating in a vehicle capable of carrying payloads of 400 pounds to heights of 175 miles or more, with flight times, effectively outside of the earth's atmosphere, of more than fifteen minutes.

The rocket itself was about seventeen inches in diameter, and with boost motor and main sustainer motor plus payload it reached lengths of some thirty feet to the tip of its nosecone. Later payloads carried attitude control systems, which were steered by high pressure nitrogen jets, capable of accurate pointing towards the sun, moon or selected stars. Accuracies in pointing to seconds of arc could be achieved — I well recall one occasion when final checks were being carried out in the Test Shop on the pointing system, and personnel in the Test Shop had to be asked to remain still so that checks could be completed without vibration of the solid concrete floor interfering with the measurements!

Since the flight was of a ballistic nature, efforts were made to eliminate any things which could cause the rocket to deviate from its intended nominated impact point. One such influence could have been what was called "offset thrust", where the thrust of the rocket motors did not pass directly through the rocket centre of gravity. To counteract this tendency, later ballistic rockets were fitted with four small short burning time thrusters which imparted a rolling motion to the rocket after it had left the launcher. This tended to cancel out any offset thrust effect and improved impact point prediction.

It is fair to say that a large percentage of staff employed on the site of the Weapons Research Establishment at Salisbury, with any connection with Woomera, would almost certainly have had involvement at some time with old Skylark. Everybody's friend.

In addition, many universities in the United Kingdom and Australia were well aware of its capabilities. The table attached gives some insight into these exposures and the sophisticated research studies undertaken. Many a PhD depended upon a successful Skylark firing, and the success rate was such that few were disappointed. From 1968 to its last firing at Woomera in about 1978, a campaign system for launches was adopted, whereby three or four teams per year would spend some two months or so preparing about four rockets for launch. This system encouraged competition between the participants of the teams and generally proved to be cost effective in getting rockets away on time. Many rockets carried more than one experiment, and getting each experimenter to be ready at the same time was never easy. One had the impression that the ability to have all ready on time seemed to be indirectly proportional to the square of the number of experiments, i.e. a payload with two independent experiments seemed to be four times as difficult as a payload with just the one experiment. However, meeting one's commitment regarding launch date became something of a matter of honour for experimenters, and there were always twenty four hours available in a day to catch up if necessary.

Some scientists, like those from University College London, we saw often enough for them to become experienced rocket men.

Wind advice

Firing rockets made one very wind conscious. It would have been nice if it was always calm for a launch because that at least would remove one variable for the team leader to worry about. One of the big merits of the Woomera Range was that, centred as it was well inland and away from coastal effects, the weather generally was stable, and in the mornings winds were nearly always light. This made it a popular time to fire, provided the experiment launch window allowed it. The only snag to early morning launches was that pre-launch operations often required some two hours or more of preparatory work, which meant a pre-dawn getting out of bed, and hence a severe curtailment of one's night before celebrations.

There were times when cutting short this entertainment proved too difficult to achieve, and it had been known for some personnel to arrive for launch clad in dinner suits.

Getting back to the wind; colleagues at Range Instrumentation had the luxury of a visual display of the wind's antics at all times, and advantage was taken of this from time to time to check on trends in the wind pattern. A call was made once to see what the situation was, and the following reply was received;

"Wind speed; Zero
Wind direction; Northeast".

Meteorology

Predicting the weather has always seemed to be something of a game of chance. At Woomera, knowing what the weather may have had in store was often vital information. Being able to launch often depended on such things as wind speed or cloud cover, and Woomera met. officers tended to suffer from a dearth of reliable information from the largely empty country to the west. On occasions they were known to phone bush Post Offices and ask the lonely postmaster to go outside, look towards the heavens, and tell them what they saw. If the postmaster had celebrated the night before, goodness knows what validity might attach to such observations! What follows might confirm this.

In late October, 1969, we had two scientific rockets being prepared for an unusual experiment in the upper atmosphere.

Skylark team with Launcher, near centre. Top, from left: Don Needham, author, Keith Wilson, Ron Jeffery, Dave Gallery, Vic Mankelow, Arnold Oldfield, Bob Beattie, John Ison, Frank Gibbs, with Rae Taylor in front.

For best results the rockets had to be launched in successive twilights, either dawn followed by dusk or vice versa. In addition, each had to be launched into clear skies. The snag therefore was that the first could not be fired unless it was known with confidence that clear skies would attend the second launch.

The Woomera Met. people were advised of this stipulation and enthusiastically studied weather trends to be in a position to give a confident go-ahead when they were sure conditions were right. Days passed, with the first rocket patiently waiting on its launcher for its rendezvous with the upper atmosphere. At last the word came through, "Yes, tomorrow's twilight is right for the first launch". Sure enough, up she went into a beautiful clear sky.

The launch team turned out before dawn the following morning to complete the experiment, only to find themselves in torrential rain! Ah well, nobody's perfect. The second rocket was launched in the next twilight, in clear skies, with some slight degradation of data. The team's faith in forecasting had been modified forever after.

Getting there (and back)

To get to Woomera from Adelaide we had but two options: by air or by road. The latter method itself had two options, either by car or hired bus. There were times in our Skylark days when the bus use was preferred when the whole team needed to be on Range outside of the standard airline schedules, for example travelling up there on a weekend. Fortunately this didn't happen very often but when there was no alternative, busing became an adventure in itself.

Without wishing to give a wrong impression, the bus journey was almost a half day excursion, and it was necessary for the freedom of the spirit to carry on board the bus, not only one's personal baggage but other spirits like those extracted from hops, to both accelerate the passage of time and detune one's mental processes. The bus trips therefore tended to be rollicking and noisy experiences before even the halfway mark was reached. Also many unscheduled stops at discreet places had to be requested of the bus drivers for detanking operations.

Escaping from Woomera at the end of a busy week also at times introduced problems. If the exigencies of work caused the team to miss the last aircraft, again there were two options, stay in the Village over the weekend, or take the train to Adelaide. That was a difficult decision. The train journey of some three hundred miles took twelve hours. It departed the Woomera station at 6 p.m. and arrived at the central railway station in Adelaide the following morning at 6 a.m. A grand average speed of 25 miles per hour. Mr Stephenson of the other "Rocket" fame, would have been proud of it!

Having decided as a team to endure the train trip, one again had to take medicinal precautions as per our bus trips, to render the journey sustainable. Interestingly, the carriages of the train bore legends advising passengers that the drinking of alcoholic beverages was totally disallowed, and yet near each end of the cabin were provided dispensers of nice little paper cups. It was clear that the latter cancelled out the former?

The station staff, familiar with the high spirits of trials teams, segregated them in the rear carriage of the two carriage train, leaving the forward section for honest citizens. Thus as the long night wore on, and the little old train rattled through the moonlit spinifex grass, the old rollicking behaviour would reappear.

On one trip, one member of the team discovered at the rear of the carriage, a cord one could pull which caused way up in the front of the train a "whoo, whoo" noise. Music to the ears. Several of the team took turns to sound this whistle, thus disturbing the rest of any fauna in our vicinity, until a uniformed railway man appeared threatening dire consequences. Some people have no soul.

And so we lumbered off the train in Adelaide, most probably fit only to spend the next few hours in recuperative sleep on proper beds. The train trip therefore got one home, but divided the usable weekend into half. One gained a Sunday.

A good crop

There was a time in the late sixties when Singapore passed an edict that men whose hair exceeded a certain length were forbidden to venture outside the confines of the airport. Long hair was definitely a no-no.

A good proportion of the young Woomera bound Englishmen wore the fashion of the day, with locks well down to the shoulders and beyond, and this order became a real test of fortitude.

It created a genuine intellectual problem at the airport. Get your hair cut and enjoy the sights and smells of the fascinating east, savour the flesh pots of places like Bugis Street; or twiddle your fingers in the airport lounge? It was a dilemma.

Generally the hair won, on principle. But for others the temptation was too great and they arrived with tales of high adventure, such as the time a small group booked an exhibition, an erotic experience, awful to contemplate. It involved them arranged about a bed upon which two ladies did unusual things with a cucumber. The performance was somewhat marred by the consternation of the exhibitors that a female was present in the audience. Such treats were supposed to be for men only.

Don't touch

For rockets such as Skylark, one had a team member called the priming monitor, whose duty it was, during a launch sequence, to operate certain switches which controlled operations within the rocket when it was on the launcher; to check for correct responses, and also to have some override capability if automatic switching failed to operate at the correct time.

As part of this ground control system, during on launcher testing the monitor had a button on the payload monitor's console which when pressed allowed him to manually extract the umbilical arm from the rocket. This meant that should automatic extraction of the umbilical for some reason fail, then manual retraction could be carried out. This could prove vital, since non retraction of the large umbilical arm would damage the tail fin assembly as it rose past.

The umbilical in rocket systems does a bit more than that of its human counterpart. It not only provides energy to the rocket's internal black boxes, so conserving internal supplies for its life after launch, but also allows the launch team to monitor various physical functions within the rocket, to be confident it is fit to have a life of its own.

This particular umbilical was rather hefty. The long arm, with plug attached, was extracted by pneumatics, and quickly too, because it had to beat the tail fins of the rocket as they swept by. To operate the extraction when personnel were working nearby could at the very least cause someone a nasty surprise.

On one occasion an inexperienced operator was being drilled in the button pushing art during practice for the real thing the next day. As he was coached through the procedure, pushing the various buttons and noting responses from the rocket, he was told, "don't push this one yet".

"You mean this one?" he said, pushing it, followed by immediate cries of anguish over the intercom from the launcher! The launcher preparation team were busy at that time working in the vicinity of said umbilical. Fortunately their injury was psychological only, but this proved to be that payload monitor's only launch experience.

Dangerous exports

As stated before, one of the great attributes of the Woomera Range was its ability to recover the bits and pieces of rockets after they had returned to earth. So, after each firing or series of firings, the recovered remains were routinely packaged and returned to U.K. headquarters for post flight inspection. The few exceptions were those stray bodies that chose the thin crust of salt pans as their impact point, and disappeared forever in the squelch beneath the surface. Recovery was usually so efficient that some payloads which used parachutes to break their fall, were recovered hundreds of kilometres downrange with their insides still happily ticking away.

It came as no great surprise therefore, to be confronted one day with a telex from the U.K. which read in stern tones, "Do not, under any circumstances, send us any more redback spiders in the recovered pieces!"

It is easy to understand this reluctance to accept this one of the less endearing species of Australian fauna. Had it been of the genus stumpy lizard, the reaction may have been more enthusiastic. The recipients of the telex however, were left to ponder that the odd spider exchange might have been fair trade for many of the things historically our U.K. friends had been kind enough in the past to bestow in this direction. Like rabbits, foxes, atomic bombs, even the odd Pom or two. But

you don't bite the hand that feeds you — not even by proxy, by redback spider.

From then on, all potential travellers within boxes were given the Qantas spray can treatment.

Snakes, for the use of

Work was proceeding steadily towards a launch. Everyone was busy at something or other, getting ready for final preparation and for loading the following day.

A phone in the office in the Test Shop rang. It was Keith, calling from the launch bunker, the small reinforced concrete underground control room sited near the launcher and used by the launch team for final launch operations.

"There's a large snake between me and the door," he said in a surprisingly calm voice, "What do I do?"

"Stay where you are," he was told, "Dave is coming up." When they returned to the Test Shop showing no outward signs of drama, they were asked how the escape had been engineered. It appears that a convenient CO_2 fire extinguisher had been located near the entrance, and Dave had frozen the unwelcome visitor with a few well aimed squirts.

This unauthorised use of fire department property later resulted in strong words of disapproval from their office. Improper use of a fire extinguisher. Effective though!

Another confrontation with the snake species occurred under very different circumstances. In the Test Shop was a dark room laboratory, specially prepared for testing experimenters' flight items needing alignment with point light sources. A team of about four experimenters worked in there all day in darkness. Came the conclusion of their work, the lights went on, and there revealed in their company was an unwelcome long brown spectator.

On this occasion they all easily beat the snake to the door.

Sting in the tail

The rocket team included one very deliberate man, not noted for rapid or unplanned motion. A careful, thinking man.

One warm summer day, on approaching the Test Shop, a cluster of people could be seen just in front of the large hangar-type entrance doors, arranged like a two-up school around some centre of interest on the cement apron. On joining the group, the object of all their attention was found to be a fully grown and active scorpion, doing its best to avoid its unwelcome limelight.

The deliberate one, at centre stage, and undoubtedly seized by what must have been a completely unfamiliar impulse, slowly swung his right foot backwards, clearly intending to drop kick the beastie over its fascinated audience.

The circle of spectators expanded in a sudden wave at this threat of a strike by an unguided dangerous missile, but the scorpion, being the quickest witted of all, with lightning reflexes and not wishing to be airborne, grasped the oncoming safety boot with one of its claws, and stayed attached.

The performance that followed would have done credit to any graduate of the Whirling Dervish Academy, as the normally sedate one tried energetically and valiantly to dislodge his unwelcome appendage.

The scorpion at length, feeling no doubt that enough trauma had been inflicted for one day, relinquished its hold, and scuttled away, tail held high, no doubt muttering to itself on the impolite behaviour of trials personnel.

The deliberate one retired for a soothing cup of tea.

Blow the man down

It was to be an interesting experiment. In October 1969 the University College London and other experimenters wished to fly a Skylark package to a predicted apogee, greatest height, of the nice round number of one million feet, or about two hundred miles. The object of the flight was to determine things like temperature and wind speeds at those great heights in the rare upper atmosphere. It was not the first time this had been done, and always created some press attention.

This was one of the very few Woomera firings which could actually be witnessed from the city of Adelaide, some three hundred miles or so away, as the colourful trails in the sky produced by the main experiment could be seen some thirty degrees above Adelaide's horizon. (I had instructed my family in this, and I'm told the neighbours were somewhat puzzled when possible launch days came round, to see the Chambers family early in the mornings go out to the front of the house and gaze up into the northern sky! As though we had joined some new religion).

The experimental technique used was to eject highly volatile chemical fluids when at apogee, these fluids reacting with the oxygen in the thin air to form visible trails in the sky. Additionally the almost simultaneous release of explosive grenades was programmed whose flashes and sounds could be monitored on the ground. (See Appendix 6).

Now it happened that at the time the launch was planned to take place I, the team member in charge of firing, knew that two Russian cosmonauts were orbiting the earth, and at a lower altitude than that expected by the rocket. "Sod's" or "Murphy's" Law being what it is, i.e. if things can go wrong at the worst time they jolly well will, all the ingredients seemed to exist for an interesting situation.

The Range Authority was consulted about this concern, that the cosmonauts might not take kindly to a broadside of grenades as they swept past. The response was not to worry.

The launch went ahead at the required time, all systems worked and, best of all, there was no international incident. It can only be assumed that the good old Range Authority knew that the Russians were in a less hostile part of the world at the

time, and that the likelihood of me starting World War III was acceptably small!

The Soviet spacecraft was Soyuz 8, bearing the unsuspecting Cosmonauts, Shatalov and Yeliseyev.

Of course, the big space event of 1969 was the Apollo 11 historic moon landing adventure, where the American trio of Armstrong, Aldrin and Collins wrote their names into history by their involvement in the heroic event of the Sunday, the 20th of July.

The ELDO Mess (the 1970 migration)

While ELDO, the European Launcher Development Organisation, was in progress on the Range, the lesser mortals in their Spartan messes used to gaze in envy at the alleged splendour of their four star "Shangri La". The minimal star accommodation of the rest paled in comparison with the stories passed on by those fortunate enough to be invited to partake of the continental cooking and the ritzy atmosphere of the lounge and drink facilities.

In the fullness of years our team's project life span exceeded that of ELDO, and the great day dawned when their mess became general property and the transition was made from the shack on the hill to the castle down below. Forsaking the old military establishment was done without a backward glance.

Like all things, with grass a better shade on the other side of the tracks, the move as it turned out was not that much of an improvement. But an improvement nevertheless. What the living quarters lost in size of cell, they gained in air conditioning. At least here the team was all under the same roof, no more social distinction, military style. Clearly the chefs employed by ELDO moved to better things, leaving no recipes behind,

Typical Skylark payload, with Mike Taylor 2nd from left, Ron Jeffery 3rd, John Ison 1st on right, Bob Beattie 2nd from right, author 4th, Dave Gallery 5th, Vic Mankelow 6th.

and the firm suspicion was that the old cooking staff came down the hill with the rest of us.

It was suggested one evening at dinner that it might be a good idea, to improve the flow of gastric juices, if the waitresses might be encouraged to go topless. Looking around at the standards on offer it was unfortunately agreed that apart from one or two, the idea really had little appeal and in fact might ruin some appetites for good.

By now the Americans had moved in with a project not far away, and there was a casual interface with some of them in the mess. A friend and I together tried to find some Americans to browbeat during Australia's first challenge for the Americas Cup, but short ones were hard to find.

Interestingly, there was one rocket that had eluded all attempts of the team and the recovery party to find. Many helicopter sorties had been flown in search of it with nil success. It appeared to have vanished in the never never. Came the day it was at last located, accompanied by the apocryphal tale that some Yank had said to someone, "We knew you guys would find it today, you were looking in the right place at last". How did they know that?

The reverent engineer

The ELDO mess was an interesting place. If you stayed in it long enough there were things to learn. For example the upstairs lounge had one of those ceilings which was perforated with many small holes, presumably to make it appear more interesting.

If you sat back in one of the comfortable chairs, better to study the ceiling's mystery, it was a simple mental calculation to discover that above one's head were spread almost exactly one million little black holes. Having a feel for what a million looks like could one day come in handy!

The Eldo Mess building in the Woomera Village

On the right hand side of the upper lounge and occupying a large portion of it, was the ELDO bar. In the 60s and 70s you could get a glass of top quality port for peanuts, port which now retails at over $50 a bottle. It was easy to fall into an expansive frame of mind. And at the bar one rubbed shoulders with not only colleagues from one's own company, but expansive rocket men from the other companies currently enjoying what the Range (and bar) had to offer by way of conviviality.

One such rocket man was always near the focus of a sociable and smiling group, not necessarily of his own team, and he could at times be seen to place a hand on a shoulder as though sharing a moment's communion with a friend.

The reason for this paternal behaviour came to light one evening when he proclaimed to me, not very confidentially, that in fact he was the only ecclesiastic rocket engineer on the Range. For ten dollars American, sent to an address he divulged, in the USA, we could all, had we the wit and inclination, have joined him in being certificated members of the cloth. A mail order ministry!

Having so enlightened me, he patted me on the shoulder, and said, "Bless you, my son".

The select committee

In November, 1970, a Select Committee was appointed by the U.K. Government to investigate and report, amongst other things, on the United Kingdom's space activities. As part of the investigation the Committee visited Woomera, and during the visit they called into our Test Shop when some scientists from the University of Leicester were preparing an X-ray experiment for launch on the Skylark rocket.

"Tell me", asked one member of the select committee, "of what value is your particular experiment to the members of my constituency in Shoreditch?"

Unruffled by such a question, the young senior scientist in charge of the experiment replied that at the very least, some of them, or their relations, could well have been involved in putting the experiment together. It seemed to be a sensible answer to an unfair question. It must be said that the report, when issued, commented most favourably on not only Skylark, but also the Leicester team.

On theology

The heavens are full of interesting objects. For example there are some X-ray stars called "Bursters", unusual stars in that their output of X-rays is sporadic rather than continuous. Hence they are of great interest to astronomers. So a rocket was produced with its experimental payload specially designed to study such a star.

All went well with the Range preparation of the rocket and its experimental package, and the time came to load it into the launcher and prepare to fire. To everyone's dismay, word came through from overseas observers that our "Burster" was lying doggo, and not emitting any radiation. (Long faces in evidence).

Some hundreds of thousands of dollars had been spent in producing this rocket, designed specifically for this star alone. If it declined to cooperate then the money and possibly a PhD or two were likely to be in jeopardy. Was there nothing we could do to alter this embarrassing situation?

By chance, within our group was a senior person with strong religious convictions. "Why not", he suggested, "offer a communal prayer that this inconvenient star be switched on in the interest of science?"

"Why not, indeed?" some thought. "It might be worth a go, anything is worth trying!"

The project scientist, however, in a quiet way, pointed out that the unfriendly star happened to be some thousands of light years away from Woomera. This meant that its radiation took a similar time for the trip to earth. For our prayer to be answered, either one of two things must be achieved by God —

1. He must have known thousands of years ago that we would be here with this rocket ready to launch.

or,

2. He would have to give dispensation for once, for our benefit, that the speed of light be allowed in this special case only, to become infinite. So that the radiation might arrive in minimum time!

None of us seemed prepared to put God to such a test. The logic seemed indisputable. The sad, fruitless rocket was therefore packed up and sent back to England. The theological problem remains, nevertheless. Did we all give in too easily?

The twenty year shot of September 1971

The firing was a very unusual one. An X-ray source had been discovered in the heavens on an earlier flight as part of a general survey of the southern sky for X-ray emitting objects. It was now time to concentrate on a typical one, to see if its position could be determined accurately so that optical telescopes might try to discover if it was observable in the visible spectrum. This would be of great scientific interest.

As a result, an experimental payload was designed and made, some year or more in advance of the scheduled firing, based on predictions that on a certain future day, at a certain time, the X-ray star, the moon and Woomera would all be in the same celestial plane. It was a bit like Thurber's mathematician out duck shooting, with only one bullet left and three ducks randomly paddling around before him. The mathematician took out a piece of paper, did some sums on when they would all be in a line, waited for that moment and fired and hit all three. Well, not quite.

The timing of the rocket flight had been calculated such that when the rocket payload was just before apogee — its greatest height — the X-rays being received from the star would be occulted by the moon. Since the shape and position of the moon at any time is known to a very high accuracy, this promised to be a good way of defining the star position. Great! Get on with it.

The only problem was that the required condition for achieving a successful launch was that firing had to take place within one second of Universal Time on only one day of the year.

Now rocket people will tell you that to guarantee being able to launch any rocket to the special second of a specific day, shows a lot of faith not only in the rocket and its crew, but also the Range Authority and all the Range systems as well.

Would the rocket preparation be completed in time? Would the launcher umbilical extract at the right time? Would the telemetry work correctly and give the precise time of loss of X-rays? Would the weather be suitable?

As it happened, the answer to all of those questions was, "yes". Just as well, because everyone knew that the same astronomical conditions for this particular star-moon-

Woomera configuration would not return again until some twenty more years had elapsed!

Rocket trials are not only trials of the rockets, but the people who fire them as well!

This experiment prompted a piece of classical sounding verse, which went as follows (bearing in mind that celestial bodies were given coded references):

> Twinkle, twinkle GX3,
> how we wonder what you be,
> up above the earth so far,
> like a bloody X-ray star!
>
> *With apologies to anon.*

If Skylark had but one single claim to fame it must have been that it was the first rocket to establish that X-ray stars existed in the firmament. This experiment by Leicester University continued the rocket's position in the leading edge of astrophysics.

Earlier in the same year the Soviets had launched their Salyut 1 into low earth orbit. Compared to the modest weight of Skylark, Salyut 1 weighed some twenty tons, and was the world's first operational space station.

Accident reports

D uty in the way of authorising vehicle accident reports could sometimes be entertaining. Natural objects, like kangaroos in that part of the world, were a daily hazard. They liked to sit on the roads or nearby, and were completely devoid of road sense. A friend reckoned the thing to look for when driving was their ears, which produced silhouette shapes quite unlike any local vegetation; others believed that if one drove fast enough the probability of being in the same place at the same time as a kangaroo was significantly reduced. Neither method proved infallible.

An accident report, diligently completed, appeared one day with the following inscriptions:

Description of other vehicle: Kangaroo, female
Was the other vehicle with passengers: Yes, Joey.

Clearly a truthful account, it is to be wondered what the assessors down the line made of it?

One case arose where a car and rocket launcher came into collision. In that case it was the launcher that was moving, and not the car.

Plagues on our houses

Life in the desert was always full of surprises. When it blows in the desert, it really blows, and when it rains it buckets down.

Prior to launching, like the day before, it was mandatory to carry out what was called a GIMIC, which stood for: ground instrumentation, missile instrumentation, check. This was a rehearsal for launch, and was a complete sequence rundown without actually lighting the blue touch paper.

It happened to be Melbourne Cup day, 1973, a planned GIMIC day, and the Range Authority asked our team's indulgence to postpone the GIMIC for half an hour so that the race could be broadcast over the Range intercom. system, allowing all key sites, some many miles downrange, to hear how their horses ran.

The team was happy to oblige, it was no real hindrance and besides the Cup is the Cup. So the team's launch crew sat in their bunker while the horses did their stuff, then prepared to enter the GIMIC.

Suddenly all was blackness, and there is nowhere on earth blacker than a sealed launch bunker when the lights go out! The Range area and the Village had been struck by a violent cyclone, followed by torrential and continuous rain. Signposts with modest sized messages, mounted on robust steel poles, were bent at right angles, roofs were sent flying, and water was everywhere. The Range area became swampland.

For several days all Range personnel found themselves in the unlikely situation of having to ford streams to make the transition from Range to Village and vice versa, with water at times over the floorboards.

The inundation brought some interesting effects in its wake. The filling of Lake Koolymilka, normally a large white saltpan, introduced wild life of great variation to the scene. Suddenly and inexplicably, seagulls appeared in the area, not in one or twos but in squadrons. The lake and all the resulting ponds and puddles of water soon began to show signs of marine life. Strange water creatures, tiny bivalves and shrimp-like things swam or wriggled beneath the surface, no doubt carrying out some ancient programmed sexual orgy to restock the species before the big dry returned to spoil the fun.

A colleague and I, determined to be able to tell our future grandchildren that we had once swum in Lake Koolymilka, ventured to the edge of the lake with swimming gear on, only to think again when we saw the animal kingdom porridge we would be sharing it with. The close inspection was not inviting.

The seagulls proved to be interesting companions. Lunch from the Kooly mess could be taken in the form of agricultural sandwiches, large and wholesome, but wrapped in almost impervious clear plastic. Considerable dexterity was needed to overcome this outer layer to reach the nourishment within. The seagulls, being companionable, especially at meal times, descended upon the eaters' good graces and proved far superior in the skill of unwrapping sandwiches.

Some useful sport followed. It was discovered that a scrap of food fastened to a thin line allowed one to fly seagulls like a kite.

They had come a long way too. One tagged individual, when reported to the appropriate authority, was discovered to have made the journey from the south east of South Australia. Was it pilot error that drove it to Woomera, or did it know by some strange bush telegraph that not only an abundance of marine life, but Kooly sandwiches, awaited the flight up?

Rocket work had a tendency to be all consuming and diversions of any kind were always welcome. Prior to the launch of high altitude rockets it was the practice to swab them down with pure alcohol to eliminate any residual oils which might evaporate, or "out gas", in flight and interfere with the lenses of on board cameras or other sensitive equipment. It was found that the seagulls were partial to alcohol soaked titbits, to the extent that several performances of "Swan Lake" by inebriated seagull artists were witnessed and enjoyed.

The rains continued and one day, looking out of one of the Test Shop windows, it was puzzling to witness small dark objects bounding up and down about six inches from the ground. It proved to be the first act of the great Frog Invasion.

Before long there were frogs everywhere, much to the delight of the seagulls. The frogs invaded the Test Shop in such numbers that careful foot placement was the order of the day. They knew it was safer inside than out there with the Stukas. The big question was, did they come down in the rain, or did they come out of the previous concrete-like donga? Are their progeny up there now, waiting on the next big wet? It's nice to think so.

The rains and water left and then began the mice plague. Mice in their millions. They got everywhere. Into cable ducts, into electrical equipment, where they feasted on cable insulation and caused unlikely little puffs of smoke. Clever traps were set for them, a popular one being the old beer bottle and bucket trap which netted dozens per bucket per night.

Flocks of raucous cockatoos were a never ending annoyance. For some reason these noisy creatures took great delight in devouring the plastic covering used on the launcher air-conditioning system. It was found that firing rockets managed to account for a few of them, like finding on post firing checks of the launcher that only the legs remained of the bird tenants, the claws still firmly holding on, while the bodies had gone with the wind. Since each rocket took only about one second to clear the tower, the birds had little notice of impending doom. Thought was given to providing the launcher with a pre-firing hooter, as a warning device, but that could have hazarded the rockets with a near sky full of cockatoos, so the cockatoo war was continued. The problem was never solved other than maintaining a good supply of plastic.

Then there were always the flies. Flies by the ton. Heaven knows what they found to eat in the sterile environment, apart from trials people. A pat on the back of a colleague at any time would guarantee to make him lighter and dispose of some fifty flies in the process. Outside, mouths were only opened if words were really necessary. One conclusion seemed to be that their only obvious food supply was other flies. A sort of perpetual motion.

In the same month, there were no flies where American astronauts Carr, Gibson and Pogue happened to be — aboard the USA space station Skylab — destined for an 84 days in orbit. This was Skylab's last crew, it had served out its time and in February the trio concluded their 34 million mile journey, leaving the station to its own devices. The relentless pull of gravity finally brought it to a sudden stop back on earth in July, 1979.

Skylark Test Shop 1 surrounded by water as a result of the November deluge of 1973

Kohoutek, the late visitor of 1973

One morning, in the cold dark hours before dawn, a car left the Village with a cargo of half awake passengers bound for the Range and final checks on a rocket waiting in the launcher for its firing some hours later.

One individual, more alert than the rest, noticed in the northern sky an unusual and majestic object, like a ship under full sail. The car was stopped and all fell out, better to gaze at this strange intruder from outer space. No consensus was achieved on what it was, and the journey to the Range was continued.

On arrival at the Test Shop, the project scientist, who happened to be an astronomer, was invited outside to give his considered opinion on what the visitor might be. He looked in the direction pointed, shuddered visibly, and said:

"Christ, that's a comet! That means bad luck." His very words.

A strange thing for a scientist to say, some thought? Such people are supposed to be non superstitious, dealers in the truth and not swayed by frail human emotions. Ah well, each is allowed to have his little quirks; back to work in hand.

Final preparation for the launch of his payload bearing rocket proceeded smoothly and the twenty minute launch sequence ran down to zero time without a blemish. The rocket was fired, its great thundering noise could be heard from the launch bunker as it left the launcher and launch pad and sped upwards, but almost immediately it was noted something was very wrong. All telemetry signals from the instrumentation in the rocket had vanished, thus rendering the experiment a failure!

One up for superstition? This same comet was seen by the American astronauts in the Skylab space station, but they had better luck. They came home again.

The sounder

Some ten miles or so downrange from the launches on its right flank, stood a couple of buildings which housed the "Ionospheric Sounder" site. The ionosphere amongst other things is that layer of ionised atmosphere which either reflects, or lets through, electromagnetic radiation — such as radio waves. It is very variable which is why sometimes you can pick up say Melbourne radio from Adelaide, and at other times you can't.

A number of Skylark firings over the years had experiments requiring the services of the Sounder, as the ionosphere was within the altitude capability of Skylark. We therefore had occasion to visit it, although during trials it was operated by WRE personnel.

The site, well away from civilisation, was a good place to spend a quiet hour or so, communing with the real Australian outback. Additionally, team member, Dave Gallery, was an archer, and could they have seen us, Aboriginal eyes would have been delighted to see that although these white men were employed at making big noises in the sky, at least these same white men still played with the weapons of the white man dream time?

Regimentally undressed

The wearing of electrically conductive footwear was a safety requirement for those working on the launcher when a rocket was installed. Rockets always carried various pyrotechnic devices, things which could go bang when volts were applied. These special shoes carried away to the steel launcher any stray electric charges the workers on the launcher might pick up due to static electricity. It also meant that if someone touched a live wire he would go up in a puff of smoke, but in that case he would be a hazard only to himself.

At times the launch team had the services of a female payload engineer, very competent, in charge of payload preparation. On one launch, for a lark one of her male offsiders deprived her of her special footwear. Undaunted by the loss, she carried on with her work on the launcher in bare feet.

Now operations on the launcher were always overseen by a representative of the Safety Authority, under the title of the Launcher Officer; in the early days a serving military man and latterly a civilian. It was his job to ensure that only approved operations were carried out, and each project had its routine and special drills.

Therefore, when he saw this person flagrantly and improperly shod, he took great exception to it. The fact that conducting shoes could well be poorer conductors of electricity than bare feet was not the issue. Rules is rules.

Hiroshima revisited

As interest in the study of x-ray stars developed so did the intricacy of the on board experiments. A new type of experimental package was introduced in which small radioactive devices were carried to act as standards against which the incoming radiation from a star could be calibrated.

This caused some safety consternation, and much was made of the integrity of the packaging of these devices within the rocket, and the vital nature of their post flight recovery.

It became generally known on the first flight carrying such a device that a RADIO ACTIVE SOURCE was aboard. Thus it came as a great cause of humour to those close to the experiment to hear after the firing that there were reports of radioactive clouds attending the payload impact!

The strength of the source carried was likened by the experimenter to that of a luminous watch, which doesn't usually produce a radioactive cloud when dropped.

Surprises

The Skylark rocket was launched nominally at an elevation of some eighty five degrees. This high quadrant elevation, or QE as it was called, allowed the vehicle to attain great altitudes, in fact travelling to the limits of the earth's atmosphere. Because the rocket had no means of manoeuvring when in flight, since its flight path was purely ballistic, allowances had to be made pre launch to the elevation and azimuth of the launcher to ensure that the rocket followed the required trajectory. For example a head wind would tend to pull the rocket down and hence the launcher elevation would be increased to allow for this.

Sometimes with strong headwinds, the launcher needed to be trained almost vertically to counteract the effect of these winds. For some reason, probably psychological, it was taboo to train the launcher at more than ninety degrees in elevation, that is pointing slightly backwards. Probably because the Village lay in that direction?

Although as stated above, no changes could be made to the flight path of the rocket in flight, the experimental payload, once it separated from the motor assembly, could be orientated by jet thrust to any direction by the operation of its attitude control system, still however following the ballistic trajectory. This orientation capability allowed experimenters the facility to study, for example, the returns from six individual stars, with very high pointing accuracy and was a very sophisticated system. One of the last great analogue attitude control systems.

When not actually involved in a launch, I, like some others, watched the early flight path from the Test Shop back doors, only a kilometre or two from the launcher. Nearby stood one of the radar stations which tracked the rocket throughout its flight and provided trajectory data to be recorded for real time display in the Instrumentation Building and for detailed analysis later. The dish antenna of this radar was a useful object on which to concentrate once the rocket had left the launcher. It was always reassuring to see one point in the desired direction.

On one remembered occasion up the rocket rose, nearly vertical, as evidenced by the dish of the radar steadfastly looking upwards, and which remained looking steadfastly in the same direction for seemingly an eternity. The thought came to mind that at last the unthinkable had happened. The rocket had gone straight up and was proceeding to come straight down. (One always had one's favourite subconscious sheltering places in mind for such eventualities — one of the team reckoned that under the Test Shop travelling crane would be the safest place to stand under such circumstances).

As it happened, no peril or even embarrassment existed for that launch, as the radar was not being used for that trial, and had its dish parked in the off position, which also happens to be looking up, though in this case, with a blind eye! Not that I knew that at the time.

It was quite normal for range staff to stand outside and watch rocket launches, albeit from a safe distance. One member of the team was fond of quoting the time when he and some companions were watching a rocket in flight and monitoring its later trajectory with one eye on the rocket and the other on a nearby tracking radar dish. They all scuttled to safety when it became apparent that the radar dish was looking in their direction!

Secret criticism

One was often reminded that conversations over the private lines between the Range and base at Salisbury were monitored to ensure that matters affecting security were never breached. Obviously much of the scientific and development work at Woomera had very significant defence connotations of a classified nature and such subjects need protection by all reasonable means.

Interestingly, it was found that making strong complaints to a colleague say at Salisbury, on the subject of perceived shortfalls in Department controlled aspects on the Range, would most likely in some magic way lead to a resolution of such problems. It is nice to think that some link in fact existed between the listeners on the phone and the movers and shakers.

Tell me it's true

Early one morning in our Test Shop on the Range, I was approached by one of our team with a look on his face which I can only describe as one of optimistic trepidation.

He came forward with two pieces of paper in slightly trembling hands, and said, making sure that no-one was within earshot, "Will you please check these numbers for me, Ted. I think I've won the lottery!"

So saying he passed across a lottery ticket and the bit of that day's paper which listed the results.

"I haven't told anyone about this", he said. "I want to keep it a secret".

Sure enough, he had won a very large sum of money, and I had pleasure in reassuring him. As for the checker, I realised almost immediately that my chances of ever having the same good fortune had vanished forever. The chance of one person ever having held two winning lottery tickets seemed a most unlikely possibility?

Too late, she cried

It was customary, when time was suitable, to telephone one's U.K. masters after a rocket firing and give them an initial assessment of how it went. Certainly this was the case for unclassified firings. It was also not unusual to receive last minute instructions from the U.K.

During one year's operations, Skylark had had problems with its parachute recovery system, which as time went by caused a series of modifications to be introduced. For some experiments the recovery of the payload in good shape was vital to the success of the flight, particularly when things like in-flight cameras were part of the data collection system. Deployment of the parachute system was a difficult technical achievement. First one had to wait until the payload had re-entered the earth's atmosphere, its heat shield maintaining the integrity of all behind it, then the drogue chute had to deploy not too high nor too low, and then the main chute had to deploy satisfactorily and decelerate the mass dangling beneath it to a safe terminal velocity.

Such a flight had just taken place, with a very successful parachute recovery. The officer in charge of the launch had just returned to the Test Shop and made contact with his opposite number in Bristol to give him the good news when the other telephone in the office rang. It happened to be The Royal Aircraft Establishment at Farnborough advising not to launch until certain checks had been carried out. A time when being too late didn't really matter that much.

Fall guy

Downstairs in the ELDO Mess was a room for table tennis. It was a popular place after dinner to burn away some of the calories absorbed up above in the dining room, not only from the meal but also from the liquids consumed. Dinner time in the mess was always a time for celebration, even if only to mark the passing of another day, and during a Skylark campaign we would have up to twenty Skylarkers sharing fellowship at the same table.

The make-up of the above twenty would comprise say eight or so of us from the local company, probably about four or five from Bristol and the rest from experimenter establishments, U.K. universities and research institutions.

The table tennis room therefore had a fair clientele from which to draw. Now being a product, long ago, of Professor A.V. Stevens' research group at Sydney University, I prided myself on being reasonably proficient at this game with the little white ball. The Professor had the philosophy that research should be tempered with a liberal mix of sporting activity and hence all of his said team was encouraged to broaden the mind and reflexes by playing at things like snooker, cricket, golf and table tennis.

One night over dinner a challenge game was arranged between me and one of the Bristol team, to outward appearances a spur of the moment thing. My opponent had not visited before and as we took up ends at the table tennis table I could see he was left handed. The games were played and much to the entertainment of the Bristol team, I suffered a crushing defeat. The truth emerged later that my opponent was a U.K. county champion and a right hander — he played me left handed to make a match of it! Needless to say money changed hands on the outcome, to Bristol advantage.

Life overseas

The abundance and variety of life forms in the desert area, and their ability to survive, were very impressive. It seemed that every square foot of ground up there contained the seeds of life. What looked to the casual glance like an ordinary piece of dirt, appears in reality to be a repository of latent life.

To demonstrate this, a visiting experimenter from U.K. once returned to England with a small scraping of dirt from outside the Test Shop, the sample being taken quite at random from the acres he had at his disposal. On arrival home, he put the dirt in a jar of water and awaited results.

In a short time, measured in days, lo and behold he had identifiable life forms happily cavorting in their new environment. What these migrants would have made, exposed to the cold, cold ground of an English winter, would have been another interesting experiment.

Maybe an enterprising entrepreneur could market cans of the stuff, with simple directions like — add water only and create your own life. Fifty seven varieties?

R&R in Adelaide

A fter a demanding week's work at Woomera, the magnetic lure of a weekend in Adelaide and its environs was too great a temptation for the visiting scientists, technicians and university students from England to withstand. It was an opportunity to recharge batteries, exchange the cloth of the Woomera monastery for high jinks, and think of things untechnical.

Some achieved lasting memory for unusual achievements. Like the two who drove up in the hills to a National Park in a hire car, locked the steering, and when the time came to return found they had lost the keys. Any normal person would call that quits, but not these two. With time being no object they contrived to start the engine and with a minimal play left in the steering, by backing and filling on corners, and a weather eye open for police, managed to get the car back to town.

Another two likely lads, in search of a new experience, or relief as the ads have it, ventured into an Adelaide massage parlour. Apparently the goods on offer were such that the

bold pair, on seeing one of the ladies bend over and thus displaying her wares, decided there were better things in life and headed for the door. Relief came from escape.

Water-skiing became a regular pastime for some. That is until one key member of the team appeared for the early Monday morning aircraft in a wheel chair. The sport was subsequently discouraged.

Others put their free time to advantage by taking up craft activities such as leather work or by indulging in grazing in the grape pastures of the Barossa Valley.

No one was ever really lost. Some were misled, some even misplaced, but generally that Monday aircraft was full of satisfied customers.

Follow me, quickly

Security at the Range was extremely tight. A vetting process took place somewhere, and you were either acceptable or not. There were however some grey areas. For obvious reasons the unacceptable ones never came to the trials team's notice, but there was one unusual case where the service of a vital foreign specialist was only permitted provided it was guaranteed that he be escorted at all times, by nominated personnel, when on Range. This didn't appear on face value too difficult a responsibility, the experiment could not be assured without him, so it was agreed.

Escorting at all times meant just that, you stuck to him like glue. What wasn't appreciated until the time soon came, was that if he wished to go to the lavatory, then his escort was obliged to follow suit. Not only that, but should the escort have a similar inclination, he either had to find a replacement, or invite the uncleared one to accompany him there also.

A very friendly situation

Another very different situation arose one day. A classified project had suffered the failure of one of its black boxes for some obscure technical reason, and to avoid unnecessary delay in its repair it was decided that I should carry it back to base at Adelaide where facilities existed to get it well again. Transporting classified equipment by hand rather than by official procedure required security sanction and hence the local authorities were approached for approval. Yes, this could be done, it was readily agreed, but it was suggested that a side arm be carried as well.

With no wild west ancestry to fall back on, the offer was declined and the item was passed over to official despatch.

Don't slump

It was noted after one launching that the pressure inside the rocket motor casing had gone beyond safe limits. In fact it was not known just how high it had gone because it exceeded the limit of the measuring system. Since the motor contained some tons of charge, a bursting pressure could have been very embarrassing to say the least, especially as the launch crew, with sensitive ears and other things, were stationed in a bunker only about seventy yards away.

An expert in such things came out post haste from U.K. and discovered that the rocket motor propellent, being naturally non rigid, tended to flow towards the venturi, or hole at the bottom, when the motor was elevated near its launch angle for a certain length of time. If the hole should block completely, something very nasty could happen. This effect would not be noticed during storage, because the motors were kept in a horizontal position and religiously rotated at strict intervals to minimise any distortion. The big thing about trials work is that you live and learn. No learn, no live.

The solutions found for this predicament were henceforth to cool the motors when on the launcher, and thus make the propellant more sluggish and less inclined to accede to the temptations of gravity, and also to limit the time the rocket, and hence motor, spent in their near vertical launch angle. This latter made our launcher training actions more restricted in the time available but was very good for peace of mind. No more trouble was experienced on that score and the U.K. expert went home with a job well done.

Eyes off 2

O ur trials team was sometimes invited to help other projects in the recovery process. This was especially the case when it was important to retrieve flight items as quickly as possible, such as on board cameras for example. In general, man-made items were usually quite conspicuous in the never-never. These excursions were a bit of fun, a nice change from the usual routine. All aboard a four wheel drive vehicle for a bumpy, dusty drive many miles downrange to the impact area, there to scour the virgin scrub for whatever it was we were asked to look for.

There was one particular occasion when some of our launch team were pressed into service — after what clearly must have been a very limited briefing — to provide additional eyes for a search. Strict instructions were given in this case: "If you find anything, don't look at it, just show us where it is."

Some projects were sensitive.

Loss of memory

D emon drink was never far away at Woomera. On at least one occasion an employee arrived at work one morning, by remote control, very much the worse for wear, and his colleagues, wishing to save him from embarrassment or themselves from injury, poured him into a car and drove him home.

Not knowing the history of the day's earlier events, he rang work some time later to say that he wasn't at all well and would not be in that day.

It's not known if they had the heart to tell him they knew of this already.

Two to tango

L auncher officers were always present and in charge when work was carried out on rockets in launchers. Launcher officers were generally reasonable people.

One of the rules of the game was that with storms and lightning in the offing, preparation of rockets in launchers was positively discouraged. There were things in rockets, not the least being their motors, which given an appropriate bolt could cause someone nearby extreme discomfort. But launcher officers were also aware of the importance of getting rockets off on time.

One evening our team was there, with a rocket to launch and a restricted launch window. To everyone's consternation a fine display of lightning danced around the horizon, with indications that it might approach, but at the time the sky above was clear enough to fire.

I happened to be in the launch bunker with the launch team when the Launcher Officer called on the phone. "There's lightning about," he said. "If you're prepared to join me up here, we'll carry on".

Very decent of him. The storm was beaten.

The two million pound shower

L ife for someone in charge of rocket firings could be difficult at times. Decisions had to be made which shortly afterwards could return like demons, and haunt. From 1975 we had a series of rockets where the vehicle was of considerable value, both experimentally and financially. I had the dubious privilege of clearing the rocket for launch; OISC, or officer in scientific charge, as the jargon went.

Prior to each firing, data was received from the Met. people giving wind speed and direction at various heights, so that the launcher could be trained to counteract wind effects on the rocket's trajectory. A message on one launch, in addition to the normal wind data, was that a strong "jet stream" (wind whose speed was greater than one hundred knots) was present from a westerly direction, at an altitude of thirty five thousand feet.

Now it was known that some debate had taken place by the designers in U.K. as to whether the rocket structure was capable of entering a jet stream and surviving the forces it would experience due to the sudden change in incidence. The consensus had been an unconvincing yes, it probably would. Since jet streams, as such, did not appear in the mandatory wind rules for launch, up she went.

The rocket entered the jet stream at thirty five thousand feet and promptly shattered into thousands of pieces, falling like confetti over a large area.

Then followed a difficult two days for the OISC. Was it his fault that the calamity had happened? In flight data was scrutinised to attempt to locate the sequence of events which led to the self destruction and no reason other than the jet stream was obvious.

The formal inquest meeting for the trial took place some two days later, where all the data about the trial was tabled and minuted. Inquests were held whether trials were good or bad, they were a customary way of formally reviewing a firing. To the OISC's immense relief, the propulsion supremo made a dramatic entrance to the meeting, having just returned from a recovery party sortie downrange, with the news that the main propulsion motor had been found, and that it showed unambiguous signs of being the cause of the rocket going unstable and breaking up. Breathe again.

Another time, whilst in Adelaide, a call came through from the team at Woomera that one of the company's missiles had a problem which could seriously delay an important experiment. A ripple firing was scheduled to take place that day, involving the launch against targets of two missiles, one immediately after the other, to see if any mutual interference took place. Unfortunately a boost ignition lead for one of the missiles had been broken, rendering it unserviceable, and advice was sought on how to effect a repair. The author's recommendation, duly carried out, was that an improvised lead be fitted to the booster by wrapping it round the tube, from back to front, so that it wouldn't flap in the breeze.

Time passed and then news came through on the official net that the firings had taken place — unfortunately one boost motor had exploded soon after launch, destroying the missile.

As it turned out, it was not THE boost motor that caused the upset but many anxious moments passed before Mafeking was relieved.

Flying recovery

The Range possessed modest sized helicopters and these were a great boon for the after flight recovery process. The Skylark payload, or parts of it, would fit comfortably across the back seat, and this was an ideal recovery technique when rapidly needed experimental items, such as in-flight cameras, had to be back in the scientists hands as soon as possible and before the hot desert sun degraded their images.

The Skylark payload could easily be separated into its discrete sections, i.e. instrumentation and experiment bays, by unlatching what were called "manacle rings", circumferential rings which locked the payload together.

Travelling downrange by helicopter was like a magic carpet ride. The author recalls one such flight, just above tree level, where the pilot demonstrated the machine's manoeuvrability by hounding a poor innocent zigzagging emu through the stunted scrubland, some miles down range. The bird won on points, but clearly was aware of its hunter, "chuffer, chuffer, chuffering", not many metres above it, and no doubt muttering to itself anti-helicopter, birdlike imprecations!

One of the pleasures of Skylark launches was to see them go off on their high, long trajectory, and but a few hours later meet the chopper at the pad by the Range Centre, and redeem one's rocket bits and pieces in pristine condition.

Helping hand

U p until the end of its useful trials existence the Woomera road, from Port Augusta to the Village, was an unforgiving dirt track. Specially sprung trucks were used, by necessity, to protect sensitive equipment on the to and fro journeys. The hundred mile or so of corrugated sandy highway was usually avoided by commuters with considerable zeal. Sometimes, however, it had to be faced, and the not infrequent dead bodies of cars by the roadside were a constant reminder of the road's hazards from such things as slippery surfaces and blinding dust from other vehicles.

A colleague and I had to do this drive on one remembered occasion, making sure that the horrible stretch of track was traversed in minimum time, by motoring at what was considered the maximum safe speed. The bitumen surface, just outside Port Augusta, was reached with the usual feelings of relief, and the car was headed through town for the two hundred odd miles ahead to old Adelaide. Suddenly from the rear of the car came an expensive sounding noise, and a distinct lack of response to the accelerator.

Stopping and investigating revealed that the right rear wheel had somehow managed to move outwards by a few inches, its connection with the car's differential clearly being divorced. A walk down to the nearest garage obtained the promise of help when someone became available and so a vigil was kept by the forlorn car. Some half an hour or so elapsed before the encouraging sight of a towing vehicle appeared.

The author approached the sole occupant of the machine and addressed him as he prepared to alight, "Can we give you a hand, mate?"

"No, she's right," he said, a short dumpy man in blue overalls, and he went about the task of hitching the ailing car to his truck. The interesting thing, though, was that the energetic little bloke did in fact only have one hand!

No pictures please

Towards the end of the rocket Skylark's career at Woomera the new science of remote sensing came into being and mainly due to a research programme initiated by Reading (U.K.) University, two Skylark rockets were specifically allocated to this study and had their payloads fitted with special cameras and films with the intention of photographing the topography of the country centred roughly about Woomera. This was the first time that the Skylark rocket looked down at the earth rather than up to the heavens. It was March, 1972.

For weeks before the two launches, parties skilled in geology and soils and flora ventured into the districts intended for photographic investigation carrying out "ground truth" tests so that deductions made from the photographs from the rocket could be evaluated for accuracy against the true ground data.

The recovery team arrive by chopper at the Skylark impact site, downrange. A good example of successful parachute deployment with the payload in mint condition after descending from great heights.

The two rockets were successfully launched and produced brilliant photographs of the area around Woomera and even extending as far as the town of Ceduna to the south. The detail was outstanding, showing roads, the differing vegetation, salt lakes and geological features of great interest to the likes of the South Australian Mines Department. These photographs were freely distributed at the time and a real first for Skylark.

Earth sensing photographs are now quite routine, and for many years satellites have circled the earth continuously sampling the earth below and transmitting the information back to receivers whose institutions make such pictures available to customers for a price. Before the demise of the Woomera Range as a trials venue, one could purchase locally such pictures for something like ten dollars each, which showed in some detail the layout of the range and the Woomera village and its surrounding countryside.

This was somewhat amusing because right up to the bitter end, all itinerants flying from Adelaide to Woomera by civil aircraft were warned by the friendly air hostesses that, "Passengers are advised that the use of cameras in the Woomera area is prohibited".

Oops!

Towards the final curtain of Woomera's active rocket trials lifespan, commuters were forced, owing to lack of numbers, to submit to the adventure of flying in little twin engined aeroplanes. For the journeys to and fro this made the occupants feel very intrepid.

One Monday morning, a group half asleep at about 6.30 a.m. clambered aboard their little plane. The young pilot walked around the aircraft checking it was all there, kicked the tyres, undid a few ropes which stopped it from blowing away in the night, joined his captive audience in the cabin,

switched on the engines, said a few terse words to the control tower, and pushed his throttles forward.

The aircraft then proceeded to swing violently in a tight little circle to starboard. The pilot had overlooked the rope on one wing tip!

Doesn't do a lot for confidence that sort of thing. Passengers start thinking, did he fill the fuel tanks? Did he get a good night's sleep?

Another time, on a similar flight to Woomera one Easter, those on board had their reverie disturbed by a sudden explosion which appeared to come from the forward baggage compartment. There were no other unexpected happenings and the plane landed a short time later without further incident.

Investigation revealed that a large chocolate Easter egg had burst in the rarefied atmosphere.

Prime estates

After a deluge the Woomera area is transformed. Where before was red brown earth, dotted spasmodically with struggling clumps of saltbush, a miracle takes place and the whole area becomes a lush garden of Eden. The red brown gives way to verdant pastures rich in variegated wild flowers of almost infinite genetic design; but all diminutive and demure. Well, not quite all, because by the wayside on bush tracks one comes across blatant strings of the wild outrageous Sturt desert pea, its blood red blooms beacons against the greenery.

The drive from the Village to the Range under these circumstances takes on a new dimension, like driving through an alien English countryside. Never a desert this! An enterprising real estate agent, at such rare times, could erect land for sale signs anywhere, and expect to be inundated with business. Mind you, the purchaser could well be a little disappointed when his diorama, later, turns to burnt umber.

To witness the desert blooming is a privilege not forgotten, and like someone else once said, a thing "the townfolk never know".

The old grey

One of the delights of work on the Range was to witness wildlife in its natural habitat. Kangaroos, emus, lizards and flying things all added to the great experience of being there. It was not uncommon to be bailed up by kangaroos on the road to and from the Range, and they usually unhurriedly made way for the metal machines in which the strange two legged animals travelled, with just sideways glances of disdain.

The author met a very old kangaroo one evening, having just left the Range entrance gate and passed the Kooly mess. The kangaroo, standing probably some five to six feet in height and with a pelt of leathery, well worn grey fur, stood his ground and dared the car to invade his personal space. One's impulse was to leave the car and remonstrate with this mutinous old fellow, but staying inside seemed the safer

course of action. The kangaroo languidly hopped to the driver's side, stared with unemotional liquid eyes face to face with the driver, and calmly left the road clear for the inelegant encased human animal to pass by.

One could imagine him some time later, saying to his wife and family, "They are an impatient lot, these aliens who make fire in the sky and ride in tin boxes!"

Come bowling

For a considerable period some key members of our team were social members of the Woomera Bowls Club. This pleasant little oasis, apart from possessing some of the only greenery in the village, had a convivial clubhouse, agreeable barmen, and to top it off, an outside electrically heated king-size barbecue.

The accredited members could invite guests, and therefore a custom arose that each launch of one of the team's rockets would be celebrated by a grand barbecue evening with all concerned, around the "fire", glass in hand, food in mouth, under the shining stars of the normally balmy Woomera nights.

The launch of a rocket marked the end of a complex process. A rocket was conceived, born, and given a brief period of life. Each was an entity and its firing marked the end of its physical existence. It was a good, clean and nicely limited business, this job of launching rockets.

Being part of a trials team, especially if one had an executive responsibility for a part of the rocket or its payload during the final countdown, could be a traumatic experience for some. To stop a launch for a suspected malfunction required considerable strength of character. Several inexperienced experimenters could be seen to age by ten years during a twenty minute launch sequence.

With all well, the sound of the great roar echoing through the reinforced concrete ceiling of the launch bunker as the rocket left the pad was sweet music to the ears.

The launch of a rocket, like the birth of a baby, was a sudden end to a period of gestation. These Bowling Club parties were a fitting way to wet the rocket's head, and the inside of the team's collective throats at the same time.

Timber!

The Skylark launcher, used for a large number of firings, was a vertical, one hundred foot or thirty metre tower, constructed from Bailey Bridge sections. The latter are steel channel, welded fabrications which can be assembled, meccano style, with bolted joints, to make a large variety of different structures. The Army still use the system for bridge building for example.

The whole tower stood on a triangular support structure and could be pivoted using a gimbal system so that it could be trained down and either to right or left of vertical. The rockets fired from the launcher travelled on a purely ballistic trajectory, that is the shape of the flight path depended mainly on the angle of launch and the direction of launch. The gimbal system allowed the launch team to adjust the launch direction to allow for the effect of the wind. For example the launcher had to be trained above the nominal launch angle for headwinds because they tended to pull the rocket down, and trained to the left of nominal for winds from the right. The effect of wind was greatest at launcher level and decreased with height.

The rockets travelled up the launcher, constrained by three rails kept to close radial tolerances. This itself was an interesting problem because the launcher, owing to its great bulk, tended to expand and contract significantly under the influence of the heating effect of the sun or its absence. An in spec. launcher in the morning could be out of spec. in the afternoon. However it was a forgiving piece of equipment.

The launcher saw hundreds of rockets travel through its length and gave sterling and economic service. When the time came for the trials to cease, the launcher was declared redundant, its three legged support suffered one of its legs to be cut through by oxy torch at ground level, and it fell like a majestic forest giant.

Requiem

The Woomera Range ceased significant rocket trials activity by the year 1980. Weapon system design and development, although continued in the U.K. — Woomera's best customer — concentrated on smaller systems which did not require the great expanses of Woomera for testing. Also, astronomical experimentation graduated with some misgivings to the longer viewing times promised by satellite and Shuttle flights.

The Woomera experience had lasted for a bit over one generation of men and machines. These men and machines carried on the great traditions of adventure and discovery, and it was a privilege to have been a part of that experience, probably never to be quite revisited.

Ties that bind

Maybe it was a British tradition, like the 'old school tie'. However, it became customary, at least with the companies with which I was involved, to celebrate each new project or work phase by the production of a gentleman's tie bearing an appropriate insignia.

Being qualified to possess such a piece of apparel thus became a sign that one was a member of the brotherhood or sisterhood of that particular rocket clan and one wore the emblem with much pride. Some of us still do so, though it is fair to say that some such ties may now be showing their age, in sympathy with their owners.

The photograph details my collection, consisting of several Bloodhound ties, both Mk1 and Mk2, (with the rocket shown in planform), a 15 Joint Services Unit tie, representing the military and air force involvement in the Woomera evaluation of the system, a Skylark tie commemorating the launch of the 400th such rocket and finally a tie bearing a likeness of the Falstaff rocket. The latter project was said to have been so named because the rocket bore a resemblance to the fat, happy character of lore, and so the tie also bears a rampant Falstaff perched upon his steed.

As a lady may distinguish herself by being dressed uniquely, so a rocket person may achieve differentiation by what is worn around the neck. In time to come, such works of art might even become treasures to be traded at Sothebys and the like. Who knows?

All offers considered!

Looking back and looking forward

It is the author's opinion that the experiences and anecdotes in this book are by no means unique. Everyone who was fortunate enough to work at the Woomera Range will have his or her own fund of stories to tell. It was the sort of place that bred adventure and the unusual. A place where you worked hard and you played hard.

It resembled to some extent an open air stage where dramas and comedies were enacted almost on a daily basis. There were times when things went horribly wrong and other times when things went beautifully right. Fortunately the right exceeded the wrong, probably not by a very large margin, but that is what experimentation is all about. It was a period of great technical innovation and progress, not only in what happened at the Range but also in what happened in the support base at Salisbury.

It is arguable that by the time the momentum of trials work tapered off to near zero at Woomera, say by the end of the 1970s, it was time it did. The generations of weapon systems and upper atmosphere research rockets had more or less reached the end of their particular branch of the tree of evolution and the principle of diminishing returns was making its presence felt. The UK was turning to other things and Australia could not afford to go it alone. It could be argued also that the generation of Range equipment was also approaching its use-by date.

For those who resided in the Woomera Village the tapering off of trials work brought problems. One got the impression that the residents there had but two feelings towards the government-run Village with its modern facilities such as swimming pool, arboretum, sports oval, golf course, shops, hospital and 'watering holes': you either loved the place or hated it. Many had to go. Those who hated the place departed without many backward glances. Those who loved the place hated to go. It is without doubt a unique habitation, one of Australia's true oases in the desert.

After the seventies, work on the Range was sporadic with few and far visits by rocket teams and modest Australian military trials. The not very distant United States sky watch establishment with its personnel and support staff living within the Woomera area seemed to be the interim saviour of the place. But time, as they say, not only 'fugits' but does not stand still. Already on the horizon is the probability that Woomera will be used as the test site for a Japanese designed and built 'shuttle' prototype. Woomera is such a unique and safe testing area for space projects that it is hard to imagine it being overlooked for future work of this nature. A large part of the world's technological future is in space science and there can be little doubt that Woomera will continue to play its part.

It is the author's fond hope that future generations of engineers and technicians will feel the warm Woomera sun (and flies) on their backs, gaze in awe at the star-bright skies, give way to recalcitrant kangaroos on the roads and experience the absolute, mind-blowing quiet of Lake Koolymilka.

Appendices

Appendix 1

Twist steer

There seem to be two standard methods of homing onto a target. One method, which is called "Twist Steer", means that in manoeuvring, the missile first rolls about its longitudinal axis so that the target is contained within its vertical plane, and then it pitches about an axis through its two wings towards the target. In this system, the missile needs to be able to move its two wings differentially to be able to roll, and together to be able to pitch.

The other system, called "Cartesian", requires the missile to have four wings, so that by so arranging the various wing angles, the missile can pitch in the required direction towards the target, without having to roll first.

The Bloodhound chief designer reckoned that nature has an abundance of animals which home onto their prey in a "twist steer" mode, whereas it's difficult to think of any "cartesian" animals. "Twist steer" therefore seemed the natural way for Bloodhound to go.

Appendix 2

Aerodynamics

Aerodynamic design is largely the business of producing shapes which achieve the required performance when exposed to design strength airstreams. For example, the wings of a rocket have to be able to produce enough lift force to give the rocket, or missile, the necessary manoeuvring ability against a defined target. Also, the aerodynamics must be such that the rocket is stable, meaning that should it experience a sudden increase in incidence for some reason, say a sudden wind gust, then the aerodynamics must be such to reduce that incidence, not increase it further.

Aerodynamicists use basically two approaches to design. Firstly, theory is available to predict airstream forces on many different shapes, and this is usually the first mode of attack. Secondly, wind tunnels are available to carry out tests on representative shapes, and so measure actual forces and moments. Wind tunnel testing can never be completely representative because of changes in scale — i.e. model size compared to full scale — but it is a vital link in the chain.

It is not unusual for an aerodynamicist to find himself in the situation where he or she has one experimental point only on a graph for example of lift against varying wing incidence. But theory will tell the aerodynamicist what the shape should be on either side of the point on the graph. So one uses a French Curve to draw the expected shape about the experimental point to complete the picture. (Indeed it is often claimed that an aerodynamicist is the only person capable of drawing a non straight line through one point, and believing in it).

Things like missiles, birds or fish, have what is called six degrees of freedom. They can pitch, roll and yaw, and they have lift, drag and yawing forces. There is a lot of aerodynamics in all this.

Mind you, the Designer of birds and fish was unlikely to have had wind or water tunnels at hand? And little need for supersonic ones?

Appendix 3

Ramjets

These engines are very unusual in that they have no moving parts.

They operate at supersonic speeds and have intakes for the air so designed that the incoming air is first slowed down by shock waves and then further slowed by duct design until its increased pressure will sustain burning when fuel is introduced. A low grade fuel like kerosene can be used and the hot fuel/air mixture expands through a nozzle exit at the back of the ramjet, thus producing thrust.

On Bloodhound, these twin engines provided the sustaining thrust enabling the rocket to maintain a speed of about Mach 2 during flight. The fuel was relatively safe compared with other rocket motor options, and readily available. These engines were a unique, but highly reliable and successful device. They were designed and produced by what was then known as Bristol Engines Ltd, makers of such famous piston engines as the "Pegasus".

Appendix 4

Bonkers

On Bloodhound we used bonkers to confirm the yaw stability of the rocket. One was fitted aft of the rocket centre of gravity.

When the bonker motor was ignited it produced a short period of sideways thrust to the rocket, causing the rocket to yaw. The rocket would then execute a damped yawing motion, which in a few seconds would die away.

The speed at which the damped oscillation died away, and the frequency of the oscillation allowed one to calculate important stability parameters for the rocket. These oscillations were picked up by accelerometers carried by the rocket, and recorded by telemetry.

However, the motion initially always seemed to be larger than just what might be expected from the known thrust of a bonker. One possible conclusion may be that since the efflux of these thrusters took place in supersonic flow and was directed normal to that flow, the afterbody of the rocket could experience a high pressure field from shock waves caused by the bonker stream. Such a high pressure field would add significantly to just the thrust effect of a bonker.

Appendix 5

Trials data

The basic trials data from each firing consisted of trajectory information and telemetry information.

Trajectory information was processed by WRE from raw data obtained from such sources as cameras, radar and doppler systems. From the processed trajectory data velocity information was obtained.

Virtually all missile and rocket systems carried telemetry. The outputs of all the vital functions in a rocket, such as pressures, wing angles, accelerations and so on, were fed into the telemetry system on board, which scaled them sequentially and transmitted the information by radio frequency to receiving stations at the Range-head. The received telemetry data was processed by WRE and passed to the range user in various forms. In the early days the format was on thirty five millimetre film, metres of film to laboriously measure and interpret manually. Later with the advent of computing facilities, direct tabulations of parameters were possible.

Some rockets and targets carried onboard cameras. Mention is made elsewhere of cameras used to determine attitude with respect to the horizon, cameras were also used to photograph missile/target miss distances, and experimenters on Skylark often used photography using special wave lengths to record ultra violet and other returns from celestial bodies.

Appendix 6

Blow the man down

The visible vapour trails could be tracked by ground cameras to determine the speed the trails travelled at and hence the wind speed at that height.

By exploding grenades at various altitudes and timing the flashes and times of the explosions reaching the ground, it was possible to calculate the different air temperatures. The speed of sound in air is a function only of the temperature.

Appendix 7

Typical Skylark programme

Skylark	Serial #	Date fired	Experimenters	Experiment
1	SL 724	1.4.69	Leicester University	Non-solar X-ray investigation
2	SL 502	3.4.69	University College London	Solar emission measurements Ionospheric investigation
3	SL 606	17.4.69	Culham Laboratories	Solar corona measurements
			Met. Office, UK	Solar ultra-violet measurements
4	SL 604	22.4.69	Culham Laboratories	Solar ultraviolet investigation
5	SL 404	14.5.69	Culham Laboratories	Solar image recordings
			Leicester University	Solar image recordings
6	SL 722	15.7.69	Sheffield University	Ionospheric measurements
			University College Wales	Ionospheric measurements
7	SL 729	17.7.69	Queens University Belfast	Airglow emission measurements
			University College Wales	Ionospheric measurements
			University College London	Electron temperature measurements
8	SL 721	25.7.69	Sheffield University	Ionospheric measurements
			University College Wales	Ionospheric measurements

Skylark	Serial #	Date fired	Experimenters	Experiment
9	SL 730	30.7.69	Queens University Belfast	Airglow emission measurements
			University College Wales	Ionospheric measurements
			University College London	Electron temperature measurements
10	SL 605	21.8.69	Leicester University	Solar X-ray spectrum
11	SL 586	20.10.69	R.A.E.	Solar and star photometry
12	SL 861	16.10.69	University College London	Using grenades and chemical trails to measure atmospheric properties
13	SI 862	17.10.69	Max Planck Institute	Using grenades and chemical trails to measure atmospheric properties
14	SL 821	22.10.69	University College London	X-ray spectra along Galactic Equator Solar spectrum measurements Electron density measurements
15	SL 602	18.11.69	University College London	X-ray photographs of the sky
16	SL 701	20.11.69	Culham Laboratories Met. Office UK	Solar spectroscopy Solar ultraviolet measurements
17	SL 603	27.11.69	Queens University Belfast Culham Laboratories	Solar spectroscopy
18	S 72	11.2.70	Culham Laboratories University College London	Stellar spectroscopy
19	SL 921	12.3.70	University College London	X-ray source spectra
20	SL 901	19.3.70	Leicester University	X-ray line emission investigation
21	SL 401	20.3.70	Elliott Bros Royal Observatory Edinburgh	Flight test lunar ACU Ultraviolet photography of the night sky
22	SL 802	24,3,70	Leicester University	Search for X-ray sources

Skylark Serial	#Date fired	Experimenters	Experiment
23 SL 803	7.4.70	Culham Laboratories	Solar ultraviolet spectroscopy
24 SL 728	16.4.70	Met. Office UK	Measurement of atmospheric properties
		University of Adelaide and Tasmania	X-ray investigation
25 SL 727	10.7.70	Radio & Space Research Station	Ionospheric current measurements
		University College London	Ionospheric properties
		University of Adelaide and Tasmania	X-ray measurements
26 SL 971	14.7.70	BAC	Flight proving boost with spin-up and despin
		RAE	Flight prove electronic multiplexer
		University College London	X-ray investigation
27 SL 811	16.7.70	Elliott Bros / RAE	Flight prove stellar ACU
		Culham / UCL	Stellar spectroscopy
28 SL 972	8.10.70	BAC	Flight proving boost with spin-up and despin
		RAE	Flight prove electronic multiplexer
		Leicester	Cosmic X-ray investigation
29 SL 1021	14.10.70	University College London	X-ray investigation
30 S 53	16.10.70	Space Research Laboratory Utrecht	X-ray heliography
		Tubingen University	X-ray photography
		Culham Laboratories	Solar Spectroscopy
31 SL 905	11.11.70	University College London	X-ray and electron density investigation
32 SL 904	20.11.70	Leicester University	X-ray investigation
33 SL 804	25.11.70	Leicester University	Solar spectroscopy

Skylark Serial #	Date fired	Experimenters	Experiment
34 SL 1001	29.11.71	University College London	Isotropic spectrum measurements
35 S 85	22.2.71	Culham Laboratories	Ultra violet stellar spectrum measurements
36 SL 922	2.3.71	University College London	Investigation of structure of
		RSRS	ionosphere and neutral
		Birmingham University	atmosphere using grenades
		Max Planck Institute	glow clouds and chemical trails

Glossary of terms

Analogue	Analogue data was generally obtained in graphic format: a line about a datum whose distance from the datum represented the scaled value of a particular function.
Ballistic trajectory	A flight path which is mainly dependant for its shape on the effect of gravity.
Boost	A thrust motor used for the initial part of a rocket's flight. Cast off when it is expended.
Cameras	Cameras were used extensively for trials purposes both to provide trajectory determining data and give detailed images of rockets in flight. Skilled operators at various sites downrange would track the missiles or rockets using high speed, timed cameras. The camera data would also include azimuth and elevation information of the object being tracked; thus data from two separate sites could be used by the Mathematical Services Group at Salisbury to calculate a missile's trajectory with extreme accuracy. Targets likewise were tracked so that 'miss distance' — how close the missile got to the target — could also be calculated.
	There were many other camera applications. Target aircraft carried wing tip cameras to record missile

interception. Missiles carried ruggedised cameras to measure things like 'roll angle', mentioned elsewhere, and single shot cameras — specially designed by WRE to give detailed missile/target orientation at interception.

The Skylark rocket often carried special cameras to collect data on celestial objects like the sun and stars. Skylark had a parachute recovery system which meant that its cameras usually had a soft landing.

Damped yaw motion
An oscillation in yaw that slowly or quickly dies away.

Digital
Digital data was presented as numerical values of function. A much less laborious presentation of data.

Donga
Strictly a dry watercourse but generally used by those at Woomera to refer to the arid landscape.

Doppler
Another system used to determine a rocket's trajectory. One doppler station could determine the distance a rocket was from the station. Three doppler stations were needed to obtain a fix.

Ionosphere
An ionised (charged particle) region between about 60 — 1,000 km above the earth's surface. Electron layers within the ionosphere deflect radio waves, thus making long range radio communication possible.

Launch bunker
As launch control post below. In the Skylark case this was a safe

underground room about one hundred metres from the Skylark launcher, where the launch team carried out their prelaunch checks.

Launch control post
The instrumented room in which the rocket launch team carries out its prelaunch activities. It can be an above ground room for example in a van, or an underground room or bunker.

Launch slot
Each firing was allocated a launch time. This covered the time between prelaunch checks and the actual flight time.

Light year
In astronomical terms a measure of distance which saves having to use very large numbers. The distance that light travels in one year. As light travels at something like 186,000 miles per second, a light year is a large number of miles.

Miss distance pot
Miss distance was the closest distance a missile came to its target. Pot. is short for potentiometer, an electrical device used to vary a voltage. A miss distance pot was an allusion to a fictitious device which could be twiddled to change a missile's miss distance.

Occulted
A body is occulted when it is hidden by another body — like the moon moving in front of a star.

Payload
Usually the experiment part of a rocket as distinct from that part which handles the housekeeping aspects like control systems, telemetry, etc.

Pitch	A force or movement in an upwards or downwards direction, rotating fore and aft of a horizontal axis. See Roll and Yaw.
Radar	One method of determining a missile or rocket's trajectory. By bouncing signals off a moving body one can determine its range. Knowing a radar dish's azimuth and elevation angles one can find the position at any time of an object.
Range centre	The administrative centre of Range operations.
Remote sensing	Looking down upon earth with instruments, for example cameras, using different wave lengths to record the reactions of various terrains. Also includes magnetic properties and electronic depth measurement.
R&D	Short for research and development.
R&R	Rest and recreation.
Range authority	The branch of the Weapons research Establishment (WRE) responsible for approving projects and operating the Range and associated services.
Range user	A company or team using the Range facilities.
Roll	A force rotating around a longitudinal axis. See Pitch and Yaw.
Supersonic	Faster than the speed of sound. The speed of sound at sea level is about 749 miles per hour or 1 200 kilometres per hour.

Telemetry	Missiles and rockets carried radio devices which could transmit coded data to receiving stations at the rangehead. This data was recorded and passed to Salisbury for processing. The data covered most aspects of missile performance, such as wing angles, accelerations, pressures, etc. which were subsequently used by the designers to assess performance.
Test shop	At Woomera these were large hangar like buildings in which rocket or missile assembly and testing took place prior to moving to the launcher.
Trial sponsor	The company person, in the early trials days, responsible for missile preparation and launch.
Umbilical	The prelaunch connection not only to babies, but also to rockets. It carried inputs to a rocket and returns information from the rocket.
Venturi	A venturi tube is a means of varying a gas or air flow and is a tube which has a contraction followed by an expansion. The efflux or propulsive gas flow from a rocket motor leaves the motor via a venturi. It is a means of producing very large gas velocities.
Volatile	A substance which evaporates rapidly.
Wind tunnel	A device for simulating the forces on a body in flight. Air is blown down a duct at speed to cause a stationary model to experience forces such as pitch, yaw and roll.

Woomera	A launching stick for an Aboriginal spear. Gives more leverage to the thrower.
X-ray stars	Stars which emit X-rays. Only discovered in the late 1950s or 1960s.
Yaw	A force or movement in a sideways direction, rotating around a vertical axis. *See* Pitch and Roll.